Premises for Vets
Designing the Veterinary Habitat

An invaluable book for those thinking of embarking on
modifying their practice. It is sensible and practical and its
small cost will be repaid many times over during the project.

Christopher J Laurence MRCVS **The Veterinary Record**

Good, short chapters highlighting the most important points
in practical terms …enabling practices to make more
enlightened decisions.

Paul Manning MA VetMB MRCVS **Veterinary Review**

D0474557

Pocket Practice Guides

Series Editors: Carl Gorman BVSc MRCVS and Sue Gorman BVSc MRCVS

Clients, Pets and Vets:
Communication and management
Carl Gorman

Finance, Employment and Wealth for Vets
Second Edition
Keith Dickinson

The Veterinary Support Team
Maggie Shilcock

Premises for Vets
Designing the Veterinary Habitat
Jim Wishart

Interviewing and Recruiting Veterinary Staff
Maggie Shilcock

Pocket Practice Guides

Premises for Vets
Designing the Veterinary Habitat

Jim Wishart
DipM MCIM AMCIPD FInstSMM

Illustrated by Hayley Albrecht

Threshold Press

First published 2002 by
Threshold Press Ltd, 152 Craven Road
Newbury, Berks RG14 5NR
Phone: 01635-230272 Fax: 01635-44804
email: publish@threshold-press.co.uk
www.threshold-press.co.uk

Reprinted 2003

ISBN 1-903152-09-7

Typeset by Threshold Press Ltd
Printed in England by Biddles Ltd, Guildford and Kings Lynn

The Illustrator
Hayley Albrecht obtained an honours degree in silversmithing at
Loughborough in 1996 and has worked in this field and as an artist
ever since. She was an award winner at the Society of Equestrian
Artists annual exhibition at Christies in 2000.

Contents

List of Figures

Introduction

Faced with the prospect of putting together a book about veterinary practice design, I began with a review of previous and current projects. Rather than remain insular I looked across the industry and to the range of new ideas and changing attitudes. I was immediately struck by the speed of change. Many of these changes are quite subtle but highly significant in practical terms. This, in part, may be because every project brings new challenges and new thinking finds new ways of solving old issues.

Awareness of the gradual evolution in veterinary design leaves me reluctant to offer one single 'blueprint' for a veterinary premises. This would risk this volume being out of date before the ideas could be put into practice. Anyway, one vet's ideal layout may be a straightjacket to another's working approach. Instead, my aim has been to follow development in logical stages from the question 'why?' to turning the key; to try to get across the flavour of the stages, the thought processes, and conflicts. Almost 'how to survive practice development'.

Current approaches to practice layout, room links and similar aspects are covered, together with some thoughts on minimum dimensions. Often, however, the designer may be working with support structures both with buildings and working practices.

For many veterinary practitioners the veterinary premises is the largest single business asset. Some will have just one premises and, possibly, one chance to upgrade or relocate in their practice management life. This makes the premises of huge importance. Over-investment may saddle the business with unsustainable overheads while the opposite may mean years of missed potential.

If the core of veterinary practice is the skill of the professionals and their team, the premises is the packaging. Good packaging protects what it sells and sells what it protects. That short phrase sums up much of premises design. The difficult part is developing the design so that it will achieve the aims of today and continue to serve for many years to come, even as demands change.

No book on practice design could be a definitive guide. Most 'complete' guides are rarely that complete. The book will cover certain aspects of surveying a potential new site, but it will not cover what to do if your builder discovers a fourteenth-century plague pit. It will discuss new premises on greenfield sites, but it cannot tell you how to conjure up a suitable plot of land in a mature urban area, or new town.

Hopefully, however, this approach is logical, thought-provoking and will be useful to all those contemplating the enhancement of their veterinary environment.

Jim Wishart
November 2002

Section One

What Do We Want To Achieve?

1

Thinking and Planning

Reasons for developing

Before we move into detail about the type of veterinary practice premises you want, or can afford, it is worth spending a little time to consider the reasons for developing the premises. Reasons can range from a desire to establish your own practice by putting up your plate, to a complete relocation of a veterinary hospital. In most cases, however, practicing veterinary surgeons will become involved in alterations and extensions to existing premises. Some, maybe the lucky ones, will get the opportunity for a new building on a green-field site.

Thinking about your market

Whatever the reason for the development, of whatever size, a fundamental factor should be the available market. There is little point in developing the most fantastic veterinary facility if the client base, or potential client base, cannot sustain the facility created. This requires pre-planning and research, whether you are starting from scratch or adding one extra consulting room. In the latter case, however, the development is likely to be market-driven in that your existing premises cannot cope with the current demands of the client base.

We will consider the layout and design of veterinary facilities later in the book. Most of the comments and design ideas presented are relevant whether the premises are a totally new start-up or an adjustment to an existing building to improve the premises of a long-established practice.

There is a general feeling that the number of veterinary surgeons finding a building and putting up their plates has declined over recent years. This may be due to the increased coverage of veterinary care, leaving fewer gaps in the market, or the finance and risk involved. Starting from scratch does still happen and if a good location is found and the market has potential, there is no reason why they should not prosper.

Some veterinary surgeons, wanting to start out on their own, may opt for one of the new generation of franchise operators. In this system a corporate organisation develops the premises and creates a brand, and a veterinary surgeon leases the premises, running their own business under the corporate banner. The vet pays some level of management charges to the brand owner. In return, the brand owner supports the veterinary surgeon with management and marketing input. Although franchising has been around in veterinary practice for decades, the current upsurge is quite new. It is backed by larger institutions than in the past and follows a model or models, which have worked in other industries and professions. While at the time of writing, there is some level of concern about the adaptation of the approach to the veterinary sector, there is sufficient substance to cause worry amongst many traditionally developed practices. Veterinary surgeons thinking of buying into a franchise operation must do so with their eyes open, having undertaken the same questioning and research as anyone else venturing into a market. They will, in most cases, have little control over the actual design of the premises.

Growth within the veterinary sector has been dynamic over the past four decades, both in the overall rate and in the shift of emphasis. The 1960s saw growth in all directions. Agriculture was expanding and with it farm practice. Pet practice began to take off in an unprecedented manner and the horse population began to rise again. From that point on the market began to move in specialised directions, changing the fundamentals of veterinary practice and veterinary capabilities. Farm practices began to take an interest in pets and mixed practices developed facilities to hospitalise dogs and cats. These dynamics have continued with the unending development of small animal and equine practice, now balanced by a downward turn in the fortunes of animal agriculture and its support service.

A developing business

Developing markets and business growth have always led to change. Those who do well adapt to these changes and, to some extent, go with the flow. As the market for veterinary services changes so do client expectations and practice requirements. This is not just in facilities but in approaches, attitudes and surrounding services. Often the way in which services are offered is as important as the science which underpins the profession. Trying to predict change is never easy although the veterinary profession does not need to look too far. Small animal growth has been fairly relentless over recent decades. As the populations of traditional pet species begin to plateau, the emphasis will be on service, quality and style to attract and hold clients. New species are entering the pet market, demanding new knowledge and new facilities.

It is the development of the market which forces change in existing practices. The traditional farm practice which began to take an interest in family pets back in the late 1960s may well be totally small animal today. Gone are the days of a pet clinic before farm visits and another after lunch, replaced by a full range of pet services.

It is, in fact, remarkable how many traditional practices have managed to grow and expand in a building that began as a farm base. This was frequently the home of the practice principal who, in the 1960s or 1970s, was the young buck who began to see domestic pets in the kitchen, much to the frowns of the then senior partners. Gradually, more and more of the old house was engulfed in small animal facilities and eventually the partner moved out, turning the first floor into a flat for an assistant. As the generations passed, the old house changed into veterinary premises. The garden was covered with tarmacadam to provide some parking and there have been various extensions to add extra consulting or in-patient facilities. Eventually, there is a realisation that there is a need for a radical change. Adding an extension eats up some parking, and clients are forced to park on the street. Then, what a surprise, the council comes along with their yellow paint, restricting the parking.

Extension v. relocation

For many mature practices there is a huge dilemma. Do we extend our existing premises or relocate? Veterinary sites seem to engender an emotional significance which can blur the judgements. 'There has been a veterinary practice on this site for over a hundred years.' The fact it began as a central base for the old practitioner who kept transport moving by treating the local horses has nothing to do with it. The review of the site must be cool, not cold, but careful, planned and calculated. Will adding a little bit here or there overcome the overall shortfalls? Will the money invested be paid back before there is a need for more?

These decisions are far more difficult than many would think. The need for expansion may be driven by the veterinary workload while the availability of new locations is not. If the choice of developing where you are, or relocating, is finely balanced, the option to stay put can be overwhelming. If the existing site is in a good location and you have enough car parking space even after extending, there is a logic in staying put. The danger comes from the law of diminishing returns, where a small extension could

overcome the immediate problem but can only be a short-term fix. It can lead to a very expensive series of small extensions, slight alterations and minor adjustments – gaining a few feet here and there at what actually works out as very expensive additional space.

There are, of course, important factors that should be considered before even thinking about extending or relocating. These relate to working practices within the building. One consulting room with ten-minute appointments can cater for six clients per hour. If the practice sees the first client at 8.30 a.m. and says goodbye to the last at 7.00 p.m. that is a potential of ten-and-a-half-hours' consulting or 63 clients per consulting room. Now, before you start shouting at this page, it was not suggested that the same vet saw every client nor that every appointment slot was taken. It was just the theoretical capacity. To wind you up a little further, it would mean that three consulting rooms could, just theoretically, cater for 189 clients per day. In the real world, many consulting rooms are only used for four or five hours per day which, at capacity, is 24–30 clients. The obvious question to ask is whether the existing facilities could be better utilised? Why invest in new bricks and mortar if an adjustment in working practices could increase capacity to cater for demand. In the same way that many consulting rooms stand idle for part of the day, many operating theatres stand idle longer! Some practices have a habit of consulting, then operating, then lunch, then consulting, then goodnight! Why?

A rescheduling of work and working hours could maximise the existing facilities more effectively, so that consulting rooms and inpatient facilities are utilised for more hours each day. Surgical cases can be scheduled along similar lines, based on recovery times. Day cases with longer recovery times are undertaken earlier and those with shorter recoveries later. Cases that will be hospitalised overnight anyway can be planned for the afternoon. This sort of planning can increase capacity and, in fact, profitability by increasing the load factor on the different facilities.

The third way – open a branch

Let us assume, for a moment, that all such work planning has been done and the building is working close to capacity. (If it has not, read no further, reschedule your work and send a substantial donation to the veterinary premises designers' benevolent fund, care of the author.) There are more fundamental decisions to be made, relating to what you are trying to achieve, before extending or relocating.

There is a third way. That is to retain the existing facility, possibly as it is, and to open a branch surgery sufficiently close to attract some of the work away from the existing site while attracting new clients to your overall practice. If your existing premises work well and are a popular location for clients but rather too popular, do you really want to change them? If relocation risks reducing the attraction, the branch option could be an alternative. The type of branch chosen would depend on the work pressures. The move to larger and larger premises runs the risk of damaging the warmth, welcome and bonding of clients. While not feeling qualified to lay down a maximum size, the modern medical health centre for NHS GPs is frequently too big and impersonal.

There must be some limit on how far most clients are prepared to travel to their favoured veterinary practice. While most practices can name clients who seem to travel huge distances to visit their favourite vet, those clients must be recognised as the exception. Many less bonded clients would be likely to move to a practice that was seen as equally good, yet more convenient. So again we have a law of diminishing returns.

The choice of opting for a branch is far from easy. It requires research before decisions. A highly successful veterinary practice with a good reputation had a dilemma. Their car parking was barely adequate, but the clients just kept coming. Expansion of ground floor space was not possible as it would eat into the limited parking. We designed, and gained consent for, a second floor which could not offer much increase in client or animal capacity. It did permit administration, staff facilities and other functions to vacate the ground floor which would help quite a bit.

Having expressed our concern about the costs and benefits of the approved development, we persuaded the partners to consider the branch option. A survey of the residential location of clients showed that around 25% lived in a residential area on the city outskirts, or passed through it to get to the practice. A search found a potential branch site on a neighbourhood shopping parade, with a large shared car park. Thankfully, the planners saw the logic of a single consulting room branch, capable of handling day cases. Six months later the branch was opened and a significant number of existing clients opted for their more local branch. This relieved the pressure on the main centre, reducing traffic movements and hassle. The branch was, at the last count, still registering three or four new clients every day. I have a feeling that the first floor extension will remain unbuilt for many years. The next move is more likely to be a second branch in a different area of the city, again following client-based research. This time, I hope that the branch will be designed to cater for all cases, with the possible exception of long-stay patients. While the reasons for development can be varied, the thought processes must consider all the options.

Considering the reasons for development can help define the various options available. While your first thought may well prove your best, it may be that equal or better options emerge. The more complex the current business, with branches and a broad mix of work, the harder it can be to gain a clear view of the options. At times, it may be helpful to gain the opinion of a third party who can review the situation without all the concerns of the day-to-day running of the practice, or the emotional ties to sites, properties and alternatives.

Research, pre-planning and cash flows

Many years ago I met a Scottish vet who had established what had become a substantial practice within the Home Counties. Bearing in mind my own Scottish heritage, I had enquired why he had chosen to set up his plate in this area of South-East England. 'I counted the chimney pots, laddie', he replied. That was, in fact, very good research.

As a rough guide, approximately one in four households has a dog or cat. It follows that the more households around, the more potential small animal patients there should be. This approach must be adjusted to take account of local communities and housing types. Some properties tend not to favour pet ownership, and some cultures tend not to keep pets. It is, however, important to remember that potential veterinary patients are owned by potential veterinary clients; one species that vets are not trained to deal with.

Many people have tried to lay down a formula about how large a human population is required to support one vet. Many have suggested 10,000 people to one vet; though I do not know how this figure arises. Certainly, in a town of 50,000 population there may be work for four or five vets. At the same time I know a practice with three small animal vets in a town of 6,000 souls, where the surrounding villages only lift to the total to 10,000. Contrast that with many cities and you could find a ratio of one vet per 30,000 population, or more.

When establishing a new practice, or branch, it is important to review the local market. District, borough or city councils can provide population data, sometimes linked to local communities or electoral wards. This, coupled with research about the local competitor practices, can provide a useful insight as to whether there is a viable potential market.

For an established practice, there is the existing client base to study. Analysing the residential location of your client base can show the scatter of your clients within the community and suggest where the density is tailing off. This may help select good areas, or a priority list of locations, for developing a branch.

There are, in fact, many techniques for surveying clients and market potential which are outside the scope of this book. There is, however, research that is required relating to which facilities the new premises need or what additions are wanted to an existing building. The first place to look is within your existing practice and amongst your existing staff.

You may have fairly fixed ideas about the facilities you require. These are likely to relate to your own specific concerns, linked to your working day, or to special interests you would like to develop. This may be the bottleneck in the preparation area, the link between the consulting rooms and the wards, or a host of other factors. Colleagues and employees will be able to add to that list a range of factors relating to their areas of work and interests. These need considering and reviewing, if a co-ordinated design is to be achieved.

Visits to other practices can open your eyes about practice layouts, room sizes, working practices and different equipment. It does not take very long to look round veterinary premises to gather ideas and ask a few questions. Seeing an actual consulting room 2.9 m by 2.7 m to see if it would be large enough for your purposes is far better than trying to imagine the size from a plan using a scale ruler. Walking the links between various rooms to see how they work is, again, more effective than a review of a drawing. On many projects we try to persuade clients to take a tour with us around two or three practices we have designed. While this adds to their costs, the value is likely to be far outweighed by being able to discuss likes and dislikes in a real building. Every design has its own particular features. These may be brought about by personal desires of the veterinary surgeons or by constraints caused by the site, existing structures or budget. Compromises which have had to be made can be discussed and those subtle balances between space saved here to allow extra there or natural light versus artificial light, can be reviewed.

These review sessions frequently prove the most valuable. They can help decide what is likely to be achievable within a certain budget and may help agree the limitations to be imposed, or where extra expenditure could bring overall savings in the practice accounts. A good example can be found where a practice is renting accommodation for assistants, lay staff or locums. That expenditure may be saved or reduced by developing the accommodation within the new or extended premises. A few hundred pounds a month spent on a rented house or flat could be diverted into loan repayments on an enlarged veterinary centre which has the accommodation within and will be a capital asset for the practice or partners. This could well end up with a situation whereby an extra hundred pounds per month on the loan for new premises or extension could save three times that per month on rent.

Cash flows and budgets

Budgets, cash flows and funding are key areas of pre-planning and research. Great care must be taken to avoid your dreams running away with the financial reality of repaying the loan from practice profits and one of the best approaches is to prepare cash-flow forecasts based on a computer spreadsheet programme. Cash flows can help predict the likely cash movements and profit on differing loan levels and facilities, particularly for small animal premises where a little research can work out some useful ratios.

Let us take a busy practice with two consulting rooms which you are working to capacity. These premises can only hospitalise one giant breed dog, six other dogs and eight cats. The pressure on the consulting rooms means that you have never got round to doing much in the way of nurse-run weight clinics and, in fact, the load through the theatre and preparation room means that dentals tend to be limited to problem cases, rather than routine descaling. Such a situation is likely to ring true for many practitioners. A little research through the practice records could provide some guide to the average number of consultations required to produce one in-patient procedure. Hopefully, this could split out surgery, dentals and other procedures. You know that if you had the capacity, you could do more dentals, so we could make a reasoned assumption about that latent capacity.

The cash flow could, then, predict the overall benefit, in terms of income, of three consulting rooms, or building for four and using one for nurse consultations. The first two can be predicted to continue as now, with the third beginning at, say, 25% occupancy and gradually increasing. The ratio between consultations and in-patient procedures could predict the increase due to more consultations, with the entire exercise becoming a fairly sophisticated model. The effect of price adjustments could predict income and profits, with new income streams developing from nurse consultations and increased dentistry. On the cost side, the predicted loan rates can be introduced to check the likely final effect on the bottom line profits. I have a spreadsheet set up with the various income centres, including various consulting rooms, theatres, dental areas and nurse clinics, plus a broad range of cost headings.

This approach to pre-planning can warn against over-enthusiasm or give confidence that your approach is on the right lines. The projections developed will be a useful part of the presentation to potential funders, demonstrating that you have done your planning and considered the financial implications.

In all this planning and research, it is vital to address the question of who must be satisfied? From a financial point of view, your predictions and planning must satisfy the banks which are providing the funding. The design and facilities must satisfy you, your partners or veterinary colleagues and your staff. The prospect of extending or relocating can prove a great motivator within the practice, if handled well with a team approach.

All the excitement of research and pre-planning must not forget the final arbiter. That is the client. The ultimate success of your investment will be down to the reaction of your existing and prospective clients. This group of outsiders will judge your development by their actions, hopefully by visiting more often, telling their friends, or being influenced by marketing and public perceptions. They must not be forgotten through the planning process or left behind in the drive for high-tech facilities and new toys. Clients and potential clients are your market. It is they who will bring your investment to life.

2

Location and Site-Finding

The search for a new site for veterinary premises can be a long and frustrating slog. The decision to relocate or develop a new branch has finally been made and you now want some action. This is when you find that there are no sites available that seem to suit your requirements. There is a danger that the dream of a brand new building can begin to run away with your original objective, which was to develop a new site. While the ideal might be a totally new building, that is not the only solution available.

If you are determined that you will not accept the idea of a converted building, you may be lengthening your search, or missing out on some superb locations. Some buildings do convert very well and may offer savings or even attractive regeneration grants.

Deciding on the potential location

Long before the government started to triple the word 'education' to emphasise their manifesto priorities, the veterinary profession had the phrase 'location, location, location' relating to practice success. A well-signed veterinary practice in a prominent location visible from a main feeder road, and you need little advertising to make the community aware you exist. That could be a significant percentage of your promotional budget saved – to spend on clinical capabilities.

If you are relocating an existing centre you should have researched your client base. Any relocation will please some clients and annoy others. The aim is to please as many as possible while annoying very few and, hopefully, not enough to make them think of going elsewhere. Whilst you are unlikely to be able to secure the absolutely ideal location, because it is occupied already, you should be aware of the benefits of a prominent site.

Accessibility

The ideal location must be accessible, as well as prominent. Being able to find the premises is one thing, gaining access and parking can be quite another. Some developing towns have dual carriageways cut through areas with highly noticeable buildings along either side. How you get to them may be much harder to fathom.

The vast majority of clients, often in excess of 95%, will travel by car or would if they could park. If your practice has difficult parking and a neighbouring practice has a good car park, people will drive past you to get to your neighbour. Yes, personality, consulting room manner and clinical reputation may help limit the level of 'drive by' clients, but clinical excellence comes a poor second to convenience.

Many years ago we undertook a client survey for a practice in a Yorkshire town. One of the questions related to travel, and the partners were convinced that the bus stop outside brought many of their clients. Within 200 yards there were rows of brick-built terrace houses with front steps onto the pavement, and the area was mature and far from wealthy. The survey results suggested that less than two per cent of clients walked to the surgery and a similar number travelled by bus. The practice did not believe the results, even though the response level was encouraging and the sample quite large It was agreed that we would take a snap survey during a busy consulting period. Sitting in a car in the ample car park we observed every caller to the practice over a two-hour period. If I recall, one person arrived by bus without a visible animal and, just after the two hours was up, someone walked up the road with a dog. The snap survey convinced us that the original poll had been right; though I am not too sure that the partners would ever be prepared to believe it!

The search process

Some practices are lucky, they seem to avoid the growing problems of the current location and, one day, a new site appears from nowhere and all partners agree to go for it. This may seem like utopia, but it does seem to happen occasionally. At the other extreme is the practice in Leicestershire where the partners had decided they needed to move. Shortly afterwards, possibly on his way home from the partners' meeting, the senior partner saw the ideal premises, a large family house. One minor problem, which did not stop him, was the fact the house was occupied and, just to make it a little harder, it was not on the market. Not to be deterred, the partner stopped his car, walked up the path and knocked on the door. The deal was soon done and the practice relocated to the new site.

Enough of these fairy tales, even if they are true. The search for a potential site is rarely easy and, to a greater extent, the relocation clock does not start ticking until the site is found. The logical first move is to visit the property agents, both residential and commercial. Of course, there is a risk that word will get out if you contact them direct, or that they will make assumptions on the type of site or property you require. Such assumptions are, normally, made on a knowledge level close to absolute zero.

When searching for new veterinary locations we try to make a judgement about the value of secrecy and, when it is better to avoid the word 'vet', we use a different trading name. Normally we include some type of site or property brief, covering size, parking and the like. Even with all our care and efforts we find that the property-selling professions are not the sharks of legend; more, in truth, like the sloth. This is particularly true when property markets are buoyant and commission easily earned. Knowing that gaining information from agents can be akin to drawing teeth is a useful starter. It serves as a reminder that we are the ones wanting the new site and we must keep reminding them of our interest in any suitable location. Properties, and open sites, come and go. Just because you have told agents once, does not mean that they will think of you when a potential location becomes available, so do not rely on one contact.

One of the most effective search methods is to buy a local street plan and to drive around the area with your eyes and mind open. By all means scrub out areas you really do not want to consider, but have logical reasons for the initial rejection. Do not just look for signboards, but do make a note of the details and follow up any you see. Look for vacant plots, unoccupied properties that could be of interest or dilapidated properties on interesting sites. While even I might stop short of knocking on a door of an occupied site with potential and I only said might, I would not be concerned about asking a neighbour 'who owns that place next door?'

Local authorities

Planning is the role of the local authority, normally borough or district councils. Where unitary authorities exist this may be a city council or metropolitan council. These authorities have a duty to prepare and publish a local plan, which gives guidance to the development of their area of responsibility. Local plans present the way which it is hoped, and encouraged, that the area will develop. It lists areas where no commercial development should take place, where mixed developments are encouraged, areas of greenbelts and suchlike. The information will be linked to specific policy statements agreed by the council.

Most local authorities publish their current local plan for a relatively modest figure, say around the £30 mark. This, depending on the

---

Table 1
Development categories and building classifications

Code	Category	Notes
A1	Shops	All retail, including superstores, travel agents, hairdressers, etc. excludes car showrooms
A2	Finance & professional services	Banks, building societies, betting offices, estate agents
A3	Food & drink	Restaurants, pubs, wine bars, take-aways
B1	Business use	a) Offices (except A2)* b) R & D* c) Light industry* *(Businesses which could be undertaken in residential areas – no noise, vibration, fumes, smells, etc)
B2	General industry	Tends to be heavier industry
B3–B7		Special industrial uses
B8	Storage & distribution	Warehouses, logistics, cash & carry
C1	Hotels	Hotels & hostels
C2	Residential institutional	Hospitals, nursing homes, residential schools
C3	Dwelling house	Generally 1–6 person dwellings
D1	Non-residential institutions	Public halls, churches, museums, & medical services
D2	Assembly & leisure	Cinemas, sports halls, casinos/bingo
	Sui generis	Do not fit the above, i.e. car showrooms, laundrettes, amusement arcades, etc.

N.B. Veterinary premises could be considered as **sui generis**, B1 or D1, depending on the attitude of the local authority.

timing, may be a draft submission or a final (deposit) version. No matter, it does present a guide. Local plans can provide very useful guidance of areas, possibly previous greenbelts, which are being opened up to expand the urban area. They could also give a useful guide to locations where a veterinary development may be very difficult in planning policy terms.

While the local plan is a valuable guide, that is all it is. Do not be put off trying to develop in an area which is zoned in any particular category. This is because 'veterinary premises' do not have a clearly defined category. They are considered as *sui generis*, whatever that actually means.

Veterinary premises are businesses which are suitable for development within a residential area. This could put them in category BI. Often, however, local authorities class them with medical centres, which fall in DI. In fact, we have found we can make a case for a veterinary practice in almost any category, so we come back to the site and location.

The planning department of the local authority may also be able to advise on possible sites, or put you in contact with developers who need a mix of uses, as well as acres of housing. Other departments within the local

authority, such as economic development, may be useful contacts both for potential sites and funding support.

Where there is no particular concern about the word getting out that you want to develop a new site, why not let it be known? You may well find that someone with a potential site comes to you. The fact that you want a new site may just be the spur someone needs as the key to getting land passed for development. Why not try a few sentences within a practice newsletter?

It may well be that the first site you come across will be ideal and everything may progress without a hitch. That is not always the case. In many parts of the country development sites are at a premium and you may be competing against some powerful opposition. The ideal sites for many veterinary practices would suit a fast food drive-thru restaurant. One firm, in particular, will outbid anyone for the right site. They are just one firm, many other local businesses are likely to be just as keen to relocate as you are, and may be prepared to bid well over the odds.

Making an offer

When you find your ideal site, or you have settled on the next best thing, you need to make an offer. This alone can be a traumatic exercise. Any offer should be 'subject to contract' and, for that matter, planning consent and survey. Remember, any bank funding the project will almost certainly want an independent valuation by someone on their 'list'. You may not have time to wait for that survey when land markets are buoyant.

Most land and property is placed on the market at a price somewhat higher than true expectations. This is normally above valuation and certainly above the price the owner will accept. One disadvantage the veterinary profession always has to face is that there will almost always be a need for a planning application for change of use. Someone selling a plot of B1 land may be happy to sell for ten per cent below the asking price, but will they wait for you to gain planning consent and accept ten per cent less? What happens if you have gone for planning consent, and spent all the money developing the layout and funding the application, only to find that you are gazumped? There is a fine balance to be drawn between the price you offer and the landowner's willingness to wait. Some deal with a six-month option may well be useful.

Checking out the site

Linked to the initial offer and survey should be a process of checking the availability of mains services such as water, drainage, electricity and gas. Normally, where you are converting an existing building certain services will be connected but should be checked out to see if they are adequate. A greenfield site, on the other hand, may be a long way from any services and the cost of linking your site to the supply may make it all look far less interesting. One of the most difficult can be main sewerage and you may be forced to opt for a septic tank or even a cesspit. If, however, the site is part of a larger development, mains services are often part of the purchase package, at least to the adjoining road if not on the actual plot.

Another potential cost can occur with the so-called brownfield sites. These are sites which have had previous uses and you are purchasing the building or a cleared site for your development. The problem can come from the previous use, which may have contaminated the land, including the soil below the surface. Many old industrial processes were highly toxic compared with the standards expected today, and an environmental impact assessment may well be needed early in the process. Old petrol filling stations, tanneries, dyeworks and a host of factory sites can be hugely costly in terms of cleaning up to an acceptable standard.

There is an obvious need to measure up the site to check all dimensions and decide where to position your new building. It is surprising how much of a particular plot may be difficult to use effectively due to the position of the access, awkward corners and other factors. Where a building is to be sited between others or close to a road junction, the local authority or highways department may specify a building line. This is the most forward position the structure may be positioned on the site to match with the neighbours or to allow visibility along the road or around a corner.

These factors relate to the surface of the site. Other factors, unforeseen, may affect the potential land usage or add to the cost of any proposed development. First, there may be underground installations, such as sewer pipes, culverts, electricity cables or gas supplies. Some of these may restrict the way in which buildings can be positioned or cause extra costs.

Britain is a highly populated, historic island. Human habitation goes back thousands of years and few areas, including so called 'greenfield' sites, have not been affected by occupation at some stage. Since the early 1990s planning guidelines have included archaeology, with set approaches to development. In fact almost all archaeological projects undertaken in Britain are only carried out because developers wish to destroy what is there to erect a new structure. All existing archaeology must be assessed and recorded, before it is damaged by modern foundations.

Early in the planning process the risk of archaeological remains being found on the site must be assessed. If the proposed building is within an ancient settlement the risk is high and the planners may place certain conditions on a planning application. Where archaeological evaluation is required, it may begin with a desktop assessment. This is researching local maps and records as a preliminary review. This may lead to a requirement for on-site excavations, whether evaluation trenches or a full-scale dig. Alternatively, you may be required to have an archaeological watching brief when foundation trenches are being dug. There, the big risk is that they find something interesting and demand further investigations. A requirement for an archaeological evaluation can add considerably to the cost and the building timescale. A watching brief, though less expensive, has the risk of high additional costs if something really significant is found.

Other underground factors can include mining – current or past – subterranean caves or factors relating to the actual structure of the sub-soil. Often, the local authority planners will know the area where the ground can be unstable and may need piling or special foundations. Clay soils may require some modification to the foundations to take account of expansion and contraction due to differing water contents. Sand, unless shifting, can be quite stable, as can a sand and gravel mix.

Where land has been disturbed, either by previous workings, or archaeological evaluation, extra costs will be incurred creating stable foundations. In fact, most contingency expenditure within a building contract takes place at foundation stages. Once a development is up to the height of the damp proof course (DPC) you know how much of the contingency sum has been spent.

Where an offer has been made, subject to contract, survey and planning, it may be possible to renegotiate the price should underground problems be found during the pre-development searches and surveys. Once work begins, however, any extra expenditure, because of soft ground or other factors, is down to the contingency sum within the building contract.

3

Types of Buildings and Finishes

Every development of veterinary practice premises must be tailored to suit the requirements of the practice and the community or rather market, which it serves. There will be different requirements for different practices, demanded not only by the range of species treated, but veterinary interests and preferences. No two premises are likely to end up as identical as some adjustments will always be forced by the site, even if the concept is the same.

Functions, facilities and adaptability

Earlier, we mentioned room linkage and we will return to this subject at various stages throughout the design process. At an early stage of the planning process it would be useful to draw up an idea of which rooms or areas need to link to each other, which work spaces need to be close, and to have some idea of space requirements. Some rough form of flowchart can help, but start off in pencil with an eraser nearby. It can be a complicated process, particularly if practice work is very mixed.

The diagram of space links on the next page is based on a small animal practice and greatly simplified. It does not go into waste removal, separate wards, sterilisation areas and so forth. If, say, you add farm animal or equine facilities you will build a highly complex chart on a large sheet of paper. It will, however, help make decisions and compromises related to the layout. This includes agreeing which spaces may be accessed through another.

Experience over the years means that we do not always need to draft out such a chart, at least for many small animal practices. If, however, there is a desire to develop a specialist area, or utilise a different system

Figure 1   **Space links (Small animals, simplified)**

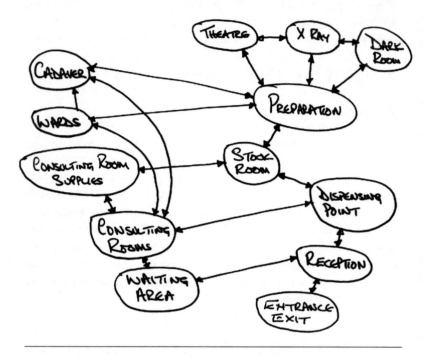

for managing a particular aspect, the linkage chart can prove invaluable. A good example in a small animal hospital was when agreeing the location for sterile theatre gowns and clogs, so that they were positioned with a logical link to where they were needed and how they were used. To begin with a changing room was being planned just outside the preparation area. We finally agreed that this should be within the preparation area with no direct access to areas outside that space. This would avoid the risk of people moving out of the area and picking up available contamination.

Planners and their requirements

While linkage charts and work patterns will determine the internal layout and other factors, the outside of a building can be adjusted to suit the locality and the type of practice. Sometimes, or even often, the position and shape of the site may determine the design approach which is likely to be suitable, as will the species to be catered for or housed inside. Whether the premises look like a bungalow or a warehouse can be driven by the land available and the local authority's approach to the development. If veterinary premises are being planned in a residential area the planners may wish the design to reflect something of the local character. Where the surrounding properties are bungalows it may be difficult to gain consent for a building of two traditional storeys, and you may need to settle for dormer windows within the roof space. If overall height is a problem, floor space may be limited by the size of roof required to cover the area.

If the plan is to extend an existing building you may wish to follow the original style to help the extension blend in. You may, of course, be forced to follow a certain style if the structure is within a conservation area or is a listed building. There was a period where the powers-that-be seemed to rush around the country listing buildings. This in truth was something of a reaction to the wholesale destruction of many town centres and rural villages during the 1960s and 1970s. If you have a listed building, do not despair. Find out the exact details of the listing, which may be limited to the street frontage and not affect the area you wish to develop. Even alterations to the frontage may be allowable within certain bounds.

Industrial buildings

Where land has been zoned as commercial or industrial the planners may want you to erect some form of portal-frame building, clad or part-clad in a type of corrugated steel-based material. Such buildings are often referred to as 'sheds' which does seem a little unfair, particularly as this type of building often houses an upmarket retailer. Many new retail parks are built of 'crinkly tin sheds' and there is even the term 'shed shopping' for visiting such a centre as a retail customer.

With the difficulty of finding suitable sites some practices have been established on business parks or within industrial areas, sometimes inside pre-built industrial workshop buildings. The suitability of such locations and buildings will depend on their position within a development and, frequently, the available parking. Some business areas and industrial estates can be active during the day but no-go areas at night. This would not be a good location for clients attending for winter evening surgeries or for midnight emergencies. Staff sleeping on site to supervise in-patients may also be uncomfortable in such a location.

The concept of portal-frame construction is long-established and can have the advantage of large roof spans, uninterrupted by structural support pillars. This provides internal adaptability as workspaces can be created using partition walling and lightweight construction. This can, if required, be altered or ripped out at a later date for an alternative use. Where farm animal and equine facilities are planned the use of portal-frame buildings can come to the fore. There are, however, different regulations relating to structures and insulation for agricultural buildings, compared with those for employment use. These factors must be taken into account at the planning stage. While erecting a portal-frame building can offer a low cost method of covering an area of ground, bringing the structure to a point where the internal surfaces provides a useful finish for a veterinary can prove costly. Often the approach is to brick round the building encasing the steel so that insulation can meet modern requirements. In some cases this can be more costly than a traditional building approach.

There is to some extent a very useful halfway house which provides large internal spans without the added cost of both steel and brick. This is to use pre-stressed reinforced concrete between floors rather than traditional timber joists. This material is in two basic forms. One comprises of large floor slabs, often one metre wide, which fit together rather like tongue and groove or close boarding. This is very strong with large spans but it is difficult to feed services from one floor to another once the building is erected. The other is known as beam and block, where the beams are laid in place and concrete blocks inserted between. This allows an easy method of adjustment by removing blocks to feed services through. In material costs both are more expensive than timber joists, but labour costs and time involved are less and often the prices end up being comparable.

As well as providing large spans this construction has a high degree of sound insulation and fire protection. Normally suspended ceilings would be used below the concrete with services running in the roof void. A further advantage is that first floor walls can be located to suit the requirements, rather than being a continuation of ground floor walls which are roof supports.

Building shapes

As stated earlier, the outside of veterinary premises can be made to look as you like, whether this be scaled to match properties around or as an outstanding statement. The shape in terms of ground floor layout will be driven by the work spaces and room linkages within. Any compromising of layout to fit a certain shape must be assessed with care.

When considering a small animal practice the critical area is the ground floor. There is an overwhelming logic in having all client and animal handling on a level surface wherever possible. If space allows, frequently used support services like laundry and laboratory should also be on this level, though they can be elsewhere without too much of a problem. Much of the administration is better elsewhere, as are staff facilities, such as changing rooms and rest rooms. These spaces, however, may well only account for one-quarter or one-third of the space required for client and animal handling.

Where the above situation matches your own requirement, a building with a first floor one-third the size of the ground floor may be appropriate. This is possible with a special roof structure using attic trusses. Normally modern roof trusses appear as an array of timbers running in various directions supporting the overall triangular truss. Attic trusses have a clear, rectangular centre running from one end of the building to the other below the centre line of the pitch. As long as the overall height is sufficient, rooms can be created within this space with natural light and ventilation coming from roof-lights or dormer-style windows.

Overnight accommodation

While there seems to be no legal ruling regarding the supervision of animals hospitalised overnight, veterinary surgeons should be aware that most clients would find it unacceptable for their beloved pets to be locked up and left in an unattended building. Any new building where animals are to be hospitalised overnight should be provided with some form of night-staff accommodation. In the old days this used to be an assistant's flat. The only problem was whether the assistant was in or not. Frequently practices find the best approach to be a night-duty room or bedsitting room with a night rota for nurses. The duty nurse can take the telephones overnight and be inside the building to supervise any patients and prepare for night emergencies. When these occur many practices have a rule that the nurse does not unlock the door to a client until the duty vet arrives.

Where a night-duty room is planned, and possibly a flat for a long-term resident, a more traditional two storey building may be more appropriate. At times we have built part of a premises in two stories, with the rest as a flat-roofed area to build another apartment on at a later date.

Surface finishes
Ceilings

When considering surface finishes ceilings are as good a place to start as anywhere. Suspended ceilings have many very useful points but the odd negative factor which at times can limit their usefulness. On the positive side, suspended ceilings offer a smart and attractive ceiling finish where lights can be flush with the surface, reducing dust-collecting ledges to a minimum. These ceilings consist of an alloy framework suspended on wires and other supports. Within the framework are panels which drop or clip into place. Most give good sound insulation and many have a high fire-resistant rating.

The most frequently seen suspended ceiling panels are acoustic with a matt white finish and a surface pattern similar in appearance to cork. These are seen in offices, shops and public buildings and can be suitable for veterinary reception, waiting and consulting areas. One of the disadvantages of acoustic panels is their tendency to become grubby over time and to end up looking rather drab. The real answer is to plan to replace the panels when they have served their useful life. This should only take a contractor a few hours as the framework remains in place. Sadly, you often see a mottled effect where old panels remain in place and damaged ones have been replaced with brilliant white new panels, making the entire ceiling look even worse. Areas of high humidity seem to make these panels discolour more quickly and here an alternative panel should be used.

For areas of higher humidity, suspended ceiling panels with a smooth, plasticised surface are more appropriate. Originally designed for food processing and clinical areas, the panels may be useful elsewhere in the practice including, at a push, operating theatres. In terms of installation and maintenance, suspended ceilings are quick to install and all electrical, plumbing and other services can run on the surface in the void above. While the cost may seem dearer than a painted ceiling, there is no need to have plasterboard or plaster above. Often the costs will balance out over a more traditional approach with quick and easy access for maintenance and additions. Suspended ceilings are an ideal companion with pre-stressed concrete floor slabs in new buildings.

My only real reservation about suspended ceilings is within operating theatres, where I tend to opt for a more traditional smooth finish, normally painted. Such a surface has no frames or joints to harbour dust or cobwebs and, in my view, offers a greater life before maintenance. There is also less fiddle when installing ceiling-mounted theatre lights or spot lighting.

An alternative to suspended ceilings or paint can be to use one of the proprietary plastic sheeting surfaces. These are in effect a cross between vinyl flooring and a thick plastic wallpaper. They are installed by a specialist contractor, bonded to the wall or ceiling surface with all joints welded using a specialist system, leaving a sealed surface though not quite invisible joints. The big downside (and it is big) is the installation cost, particularly when compared with a painted plaster surface. The same plastic sheeting system can be used on walls and can be found in many food hygiene areas, kitchens and cutting plants. These finishes are tough, durable and readily cleaned, and some practices have installed them and are very happy. I tend to be a little wary in that I have seen old installations of similar materials which, after 15 years, look decidedly downmarket. While the surface may be tough and scratch-resistant, the sharp corner of an unguarded trolley is likely to be the winner, particularly on repeated impacts. Also, the older finishes I have seen have tended to discolour over time.

It is sometimes useful to consider the very long term when planning surface finishes. Woodchip wallpaper was the bee's knees for domestic walls back in the 1970s. A quick coat of emulsion every few years and the finish would last forever. That was all right until you got fed up with it and tried to get it off. All surface finishes need to be replaced eventually. Wall boarding and plastic finishes may offer a life of 10–15 years before they need replacing through wear, damage, fashion or boredom.

There is a great desire to have premises which appear fairly clinical and are highly cleanable. When it comes to ceilings, one question that should be asked is how often are they actually cleaned? In truth most ceilings may have cobwebs removed and be generally dusted over but a full wash is likely to be rare. For this reason there is a logical argument to go with paint. This will force cleaning and refreshing when grubby and is low cost and easy.

Walls

In terms of the potential risk of infections the cleanliness of a ceiling is likely to have fairly low relevance even in an operating theatre. That is unless ducting systems are circulating bugs or the ceiling surface is unsound, with the risk of gravity playing some part. The actual patient should never have contact with the ceiling. The same point, in many respects, is true of walls. How often does a patient in for surgery come into contact with the walls? (Only on a really bad Monday). The risk here, is from wall dirt contaminating people, trolleys, and equipment, and then gaining access to the patient.

Wall boarding and other surfaces offer a long life, high cleanability (apart from some joints) and low maintenance. The downside is the high insulation cost and the difficulty in repair or matching up should that ever be required. Paint on plaster offers a low cost, seamless and cleanable surface but with a shorter life. This is balanced by the ease of repair and relatively low replenishment cost. It may be one of the many signs of age but I tend to opt for the adaptability of paint on plaster for most upper wall areas and many lower walls as well, often preferring traditional two-coat plastering systems to dry-lining and skimming.

Splitting the walls horizontally can be quite a useful approach. This could be done by a variety of means to suit the location and practice style. In many waiting rooms where loose chairs are used some form of rubbing strip around the walls will stop chair backs gouging holes. Of course this strip can only be positioned with the aid of the offending chair and may need to be 150 mm (6") deep. In the preparation area you may opt for tiling at the lower level with paint above.

One client of ours claims to be able to freshen up his three consulting rooms in the time between the end of morning consultation at around 11.30 a.m. and the beginning of the afternoon session at 2.00 p.m. The consulting rooms have a fairly traditional dado rail around the walls with different coloured matt vinyl emulsion above and below. If the lower walls begin to look tired that area of all three rooms can be repainted in about an hour and a half. With luck they will dry quickly as well.

The areas that tend to require something other than paint are operating theatres, preparation areas, dental suites and splash-backs. Before, however, writing off paints for such areas we should look at some of the alternatives.

Trade emulsion

When considering paint we should perhaps begin at what is often considered the bottom rung on the ladder. That is the 'trade emulsion' normally applied to new plasterwork soon after building. At this stage it can be unwise to apply a moisture-tight barrier as the building will still be drying out. In a later chapter we will discuss the six-month retention period following practical completion when the contractor repairs minor problems, surface cracking and touches up paintwork.

Trade emulsion allows any trapped moisture to escape and, as such, cannot be considered a long-term finish. In fact we recommend a planned repaint some two or three years after completion.

Vinyl emulsion

Modern emulsion paints normally contain vinyl which is tough and washable. The finish is either matt or silk, offering a flat coat or slight sheen. There are also vinyls designed for higher humidity areas such as bathrooms and kitchens, most of which have some level of sheen and are very tough. We have found matt emulsion paints offer an attractive finish which does not appear over-clinical but can be washed over, even quite vigorously.

Eggshell

The traditional eggshell paint is in simple terms, gloss paint without the shine. It is an oil-based matt finish paint, used in many commercial and hospital locations. Today there are water-based eggshell finishes which, in effect, are super-tough emulsions and very durable indeed. Tough eggshell paints have many uses within veterinary practices and can take a good deal of wear, washing and punishment.

Gloss paint

For some domestic situations, gloss paint is out of fashion or favour at the beginning of the twenty-first century. The trend is for a softer sheen on paintwork and doors. High gloss, however, is one of the most durable and easily cleaned paint surfaces, ideal for doors and frames, window cills, and similar areas. The high gloss finish is not very attractive for large expanses of wall surface as it tends to look rather institutional. Doors and door frames, where finger marks need regular removal should be glossed unless a varnish finish is used. In the latter case it should be a gloss or sheen rather than a matt.

Plastic paints

Today there is a wide range of liquid-applied paints which dry with some degree of plastic finish. Many are designed for higher humidity areas like commercial kitchens and changing rooms. Although colour ranges are limited, some offer splattered finishes to add a dash of colour and in general they are very tough. These paints can offer a useful alternative to tiling or wall boards in terms of giving a longer life compared with more traditional paints. One problem we have noted is that when they do start to fail, they tend to peel off and, because they are quite thick, they can be difficult to overpaint. Some are more vulnerable to Blu-tac and other fixers than traditional paints.

Epoxy resins

Epoxy resin paints are probably the toughest of the lot. Like epoxy resin glues they come as two-packs with a hardener mixed into the liquid prior to application. The instructions are something like 'mix the paint and hardener and paint like fury'. Once set the surface is tough and impermeable though they do seem to discolour a little over time.

With all wall finishes within a veterinary premises we are making compromises between attractiveness, durability and cleanability. Durability offers the potential of low maintenance though may need a cleaning schedule. It also delays the refit factor which could be highly disruptive. High cleanability adds practicality but can appear a little harsh and almost brutal. Attractiveness makes the place pleasant to work in and visit and helps keep the punters coming back.

Bearing these factors in mind when considering surface finishes can help set the balance. The front of house must be cleanable but attractive and will need refreshing to keep an up-to-date or classic appearance. Wall boarding may become dated within its expected life while plastic sheet materials may look rather harsh and more like a cutting plant than a clinic. In-patient areas like the theatre and preparation areas are the parts of the premises where durability and cleanability come to the fore.

With totally new-build projects wall boarding does have certain attractions. There is no need to plaster the walls and all services can be hidden behind the panels. There is a need however to try to think of everything so it can get hidden away and at times an extra cupboard can be tricky to secure.

Where left to our own devices we always opt for one particular finish for theatre walls. It is a material with a surface as smooth as glass and if the right colour is chosen it always looks good. The right colour is white and the material is ceramic tiles, 150 mm (6 inch) square, fixed with waterproof grout. Boring, classical, durable, replaceable and not very expensive. The only room for argument could be the grout but as mentioned earlier how often do patients touch the walls?

Flooring

Flooring is the other major surface finish to be considered and one which can be fraught with difficulties. A shining floor which looks magnificent can be treacherous when wet. In truth, almost all cleanable flooring can be treacherous when wet. In order to aid cleaning a system with no right-angle corners where floor joins the wall is a must. This is normally referred to as 'coved flooring' and makes for much easier cleaning, without such a risk of a tide mark around the edges.

The floor of a veterinary practice takes a huge volume of traffic, particularly around the key doorways like the entrance and consulting rooms. Any failure in the flooring which requires repair or replacement will cause massive disruption to the workings of the practice, so should be avoided by investment in the best that can be afforded. This rules out domestic quality vinyl floors, particularly those with a slight cushioned effect. These will not take the punishment and, in most cases, the coloured patterned layer is a few microns thick which, when worn, leaves a white or greyish area.

Before discussing vinyl further, there is a point in reviewing alternatives. If, however, you are aiming for a hospital-status building where floor coving is mandatory, there really is little alternative to vinyl.

Ceramic flooring

Under this heading it is worth considering all types of floor tile finishes from terrazzo finishes and glazed tiles to quarry tiles. All are hard, durable finishes which last for decades as long as they do not succumb to damage or settlement. Most can be extremely slippery when wet and can only be recommended in very special situations. There are some quarry tiles and some glazed ceramics with ribbed finishes which are designed for wet areas. These are still slippery for most footwear though I have seen them used successfully in some large animal utility and preparation areas.

In terms of cleanliness the potential problem is the grouted joints, though as harsh cleaners can be used, the problem is not as real as may at first be thought. Also, many floor tile manufacturers do make coved edging tiles which aid cleaning.

Carpet

Normal carpet is not really appropriate for any area handling animals or muddy shoes. There was a phase when some practices used the tough, cleanable carpets which were stuck down to the floor. These they claimed were more user-friendly for dogs, and clients seemed to like them. The carpet material used is stain-resistant and washable but it cannot be mopped over three or four times a day. In fact, many practices with such flooring found they needed a professional cleaner to shampoo and scrub the surface quite frequently, with maintenance mopping between.

Fans of carpeted veterinary practices had recognised one important problem with veterinary flooring, which is the problem of dogs on smooth surfaces. They just do not like it! Excitable dogs seem to tap dance on the floor with their claws clicking uncontrollably on the surface. Dogs which are trying to pull their owner out as quickly as possible skate around with some risk of injury.

The only surface we have found which provides an acceptable blend of client and patient safety, good durability and cleanability is slip-resistant contract quality vinyl. Even that is not perfect.

Slip-resistant vinyl

Slip-resistant vinyl is what is says – slip-resistant – not slip-proof. If water is allowed to pool on the floor it will be slippery too. Dogs, however, stand much more happily and tend to remain calmer on this surface than on smooth vinyl or ceramic tiles and the risk of a client falling over should be much reduced.

The slip-resistant quality of the flooring is provided with particles of carborundum within the upper surface. This grips the feet and reduces the risk of slipping. To retain the slip-resistance these floors cannot be dressed or polished. Those grips, however, do not know the difference between feet and dirt so they do become soiled and need proper management.

Most people think of cleaning vinyl flooring with a mop and a proprietary brand of liquid floor cleaning detergent. Such detergents are not much use on contract vinyl, particularly the slip-resistant variety. First, the cleaners must be alkaline if the dirt is to be shifted. Secondly, some form of rotary floor scrubber will be needed on a fairly frequent basis to get the floor really clean. This is floor management rather than just cleaning and for many the idea of using a contract cleaning firm is the favoured system for the main daily clean.

Achieving a coved skirting with vinyl flooring can be done in two ways. One is to use a special profile around the room edge and run the flooring up the wall for 100 mm (4"). This calls for skilled laying and special mitres and all joints must be hot-welded. Coving the flooring up the walls when using slip-resistant flooring causes hygiene problems around the edges – the sort of problems that coving is meant to avoid. The gripping surface grabs the dirt and makes cleaning difficult. Our preferred approach is to use an inset coving of pre-formed smooth vinyl which is fixed in place at the junction of the floor and the wall. The slip-resistant flooring is then laid flat on the floor with a butt join to the coving. Again all joints are hot-welded but the curved surface of the coving is smooth and easier to clean. The coving can also be in a contrasting colour, creating an attractive edge to the surface.

4

The Design and Building Stages

Arriving at a satisfactory design that will serve the requirements of the practice for years to come is the fundamental aim of the entire development process. It should be undertaken with great care and considerable prior thought and research.

In practical terms two factors can make this phase difficult. Firstly, there is the constant pressure on veterinary time, making it difficult for busy vets to gain clear thinking time, or to visit other premises. Secondly, few vets have actually experienced working in many different premises. Combining these points often means there is a limited idea of what can be achieved or what is actually required. Some years ago I was working with a four-vet, all-partner practice. Three of the partners had joined that practice straight from university and the other had worked in two other places – the rakish devil! With the main premises, a branch and a mixed practice, time for the four to get together was strictly limited, let alone time for visiting other practices to gain practical ideas.

There is, of course, a great distinction between extending or adapting an existing building and building anew. With existing premises you know what you have got and which parts need to be altered or facilities added. The structure of the building can cause certain restrictions on design, due to the location of supporting walls or the size of individual rooms. The large Victorian house, for example, can have rooms big enough to divide into useful new areas. In one project we created two consulting rooms and a shared dispensary within one former drawing room which the practice had used as the only consulting room. The vets claimed that you really learnt how to handle cats in a huge room. If they escaped from the consulting table they could be difficult to recapture. One danger with dividing large rooms is that you can end up with small floor areas and very high ceilings, or narrow tall rooms. These can appear disproportionate and suspended ceilings need to be installed to bring them back to a reasonable scale.

It is often said that you can do anything you like with a building; well, just about anything. Just because a wall is structural does not mean you cannot remove it, you just have to support whatever that wall is holding up. In practical terms this may be uneconomic or not worth the expense. In strict engineering terms it is, almost always, possible.

Building costs

With a total new-build the only restrictions are space and budget. The modern requirements for car parking can eat up an amazing amount of land, but it is a necessary investment if you want your premises to be easy for clients to attend, and to gain planning consent. Often it is the over-sizing of individual rooms that gobbles up most space and, therefore, budget. There is a fine line between an adequate space which works effectively and an area that is just too small. This is a particular risk when you are trying to get a quart into a pint pot.

Building costs vary, depending on the type of structure chosen and the facilities created within. Bricks, mortar and concrete are, in fact, quite cheap. Plumbing, heating, electrical

installations and finishes are where costs are added, as are specialist factors like piped gases, contract-quality coved flooring, and radiological protection. Ignoring cages, theatre tables and other fixtures, we try to run a cost-estimating system based on the square metres of floor space being created. Obviously this can only be a guide, but it is of value. The system is worked on actual costs of similar jobs with a little bit added to take account of rising prices. In the early and mid-1990s the construction industry was having a hard time. Building firms priced keenly to get work and manufacturers discounted products quite heavily. From the latter part of that decade and into the new century the industry has remained much more buoyant and, in fact, there remains a shortage of skilled tradesmen. This has caused construction costs to rise. This is, to be fair, counterbalanced by higher property values.

Table 2 gives some idea of the likely costs of construction. These figures can only be taken as a guide as there can be a wide variation on the level of finish, wiring etc. The figures are for a finished building, wired, plumbed, and painted, but without veterinary equipment.

Table 2	Building costs
Type of building	£ per sq m (excluding VAT)
New build veterinary areas	850–1,120
New build office/domestic	750–900
Office/domestic first floor	650–800
Conversion costs	375–500

These figures are useful in the early stages of design when trying to balance the sizes of budget, building and expectations. There is little value in getting all excited about new premises only to find that what you have designed is way over any sustainable budget.

Tightening down the size of the building when it is just represented by lines on paper may free budget for an extra consulting room, a second theatre or some other facility. In a recent project I spent around six hours trying to reduce the size of a planned building without a loss of any facilities within. I managed to shave three metres from the length of a 15 metre-wide building, that is 45 square metres of floor space saved, which could save £30,000 on the cost. While it may add a little to the design costs, the final saving is substantial.

Although it does not look very pretty, we often prepare what we term a 'pencil draft' as our first design presentation particularly on larger, new-build projects. This is, in effect, a prototype design. It is a copy of the design, drafted in pencil, before it has been traced in ink and neatly labelled. Apart from saving our clients money in drafting time, we can simply amend the original draft with a rubber. Many design firms now use computer-aided design, known as CAD. Many of our own designs are transferred to CAD either after an approved pencil draft or a little later in the process. CAD has the advantage that minor alterations can be made without considerable redrafting. It is particularly valuable when the technical aspects of the design are being worked up as the drawings can be multi-layered and you only print the layers you want. This means the basic design can be maintained with electrical installation on one layer, mechanical on another. In the early stages of design I find a pencil and rubber far quicker and more effective as the creative thought processes flow. Once the main aspects are agreed, CAD comes into its own.

The design brief

One of the hardest aspects of design is to get down a clear brief from the client. Often we find it necessary to take the lead by asking: How many consulting rooms? Are you aiming for hospital status? What do you want it to look like? It is always helpful if the veterinary practice partners have developed a wish list, particularly if this is divided into 'must have' and 'would like'. Some level of hate list is also useful. Yes, some of the items may be unrealistic dreams, at least for now. Knowing that they exist may allow the designer to build in scope for tomorrow. One of the great things about a new-build project, from the designer's point of view, is to be able to design for the future. Looking back over the last two decades of veterinary practice would make a fool out of anyone who tried to predict the next 20 years. Designing adaptability into a new building is not just a desire, it is a responsibility. In reality it is not all that difficult, it is just a realisation that the brief given today is not a brief for eternity. At times this is not always possible, though in most cases we know how to add another consulting room or enlarge the surgical space without any real difficulty.

Planning consent

Having drafted your design, the next stage is to apply for planning

consent. In some respects, planning consent is exactly what it says – consent to plan. It is the first stage of being able to erect a building, change the use of an existing building or add an extension.

The planning consent process is the local authority reviewing the concept in principle and accepting, or rejecting, the particular development. They look at the impact on the area, whether it fits with local planning policies, traffic movements and whether the look of the building will be appropriate. The majority of applications for a new veterinary premises will go to the full planning committee. This is local democracy in action, warts and all. Concern may be raised about barking dogs, horse boxes, traffic movements, excrement, smells and other disturbances. There is also the risk that political point scoring may come into play in certain authorities.

The process of making a planning application requires the preparation of a portfolio of information which is sent to the local planners for their consideration, together with a fee. Normally, four copies of everything, and sometimes six, need to be lodged with the authority. Local authorities provide a standard pack of forms and information, together with a list of requirements. In most cases there is an additional form for commercial premises although some planners have developed a single application form for all situations. Like all such forms, some of the questions will not be relevant and the format can be a little confusing at times. Within this application is a need to certify that you own the premises or have notified the owner of the pending application. You also have to state whether or not it relates to agricultural land. In England and Wales, and I believe Scotland, you can apply for planning consent on land you do not own. You do, however, need to certify that you have informed the current owner or owners. This may seem strange but, if you could not do this, how would you be able to make a purchase offer 'subject to planning consent'?

The application requires a 'site plan', normally at a scale of 1:1,250 to show where the site is and any land adjoining that you own. Most authorities now want an extract of the Ordnance Survey plan (which they can supply for a consideration). A 'block plan' is required, normally at a scale of 1:500 to show where the building is to be located on the site, the position and extent of car parking or where the new buiilding or extension will stand in relation to the existing structures.

These plans are in addition to the main drawings showing existing and proposed elevations and layouts which are normally to 1:50 or 1:100

scale. In many respects the detail of internal layouts is not that critical at this stage but it must be a fair representation. The external elevations are more important because they link to the planning consent process.

Once submitted the application is checked for completeness and lodged by the authority. This, in effect, is the date upon which the clock begins to tick on the eight-week planning application process. Eight weeks is the timescale in which a decision should be made although the planners can delay the process in various ways and the planning committee can make a decision to defer their decision! The first month or so after an application has been made seems a dead period for the applicant. It is, in fact, a consultation period where copies of the plan are sent out to various bodies for their opinion. The local parish or town council will have their say as may the Civic Trust. The highways department, whether county or national, will look at traffic management and impact, and neighbours will be informed by advertisements, notices on the site, and letters through their door – all asking for comments and objections. At the end of the consultation period the relevant planning officer will draw all the opinions together in a prepared report. This, following consultation within the planning department, is likely to recommend either approval or refusal. The final decision is up to the planning committee. Most local authorities allow their planning department to make certain decisions without waiting for a meeting of the full planning committee. This is known as 'delegated powers' and will depend on the application as to whether or not this would be applicable. At around the four to five-week stage, it is sometimes possible to pick up vibes about the progress. Contact the planning officer to find out if there are many objections, which you may be able to counter, before the report is prepared. Delegated powers tend not to be used where there have been significant objections.

Where a parish or town council is involved, it may well be worth going to the meeting at which your plans will be discussed. This may be very useful, unless you are short of patience or temper, in which case it could be a disaster. Parish and town councils are, in effect, the same, but on a slightly different scale. In both cases they can discuss the planning application and forward their thoughts and recommendations to the local authority. They are, however, only a consultation body and a refusal at the parish or town level is not, in effect, a refusal – nor is their agreement an approval. Whether it is a parish council or the local district or borough planning committee meeting, you are dealing with elected members who are there to make a decision. You can go and listen but, unless the chair (being politically correct) opens the meeting for public comment, you have no right to speak. In most cases, however, if the parish or town clerk has been informed of your attendance, the chair will have been notified and you may be invited to comment or respond. At district level this opportunity does not normally exist.

It must be recognised that most local authorities will deal with very few applications for veterinary premises and virtually no one will have experience of what a modern veterinary practice is like. This can lead to what those in the know might think are silly concerns. It can, however, lead to some real problems coming to light, some you may not have considered.

At the application stage there is the opportunity to provide additional information. If carefully prepared, this could allay certain likely concerns, particularly if you have spoken to the planning officer who covers your area. The planning officer should know the local situation and mention concerns that the council or the officer could bring out later; if these concerns are known, they may be counted in the application.

The above process, with all the plans, is for full planning consent. In certain circumstances it is possible to go for outline consent first, although there is still a need for a full application later, covering the details. In most situations I tend to go for full consent straight away, as it only costs a little extra and saves probably three months. A 'change of use' application is, in fact, a full application in most situations. The decision of the planning department may be refusal, approval or conditional approval. In most cases we would expect certain conditions to be applied, such as landscaping and planting schemes and similar requirements. Some conditions can be restrictive, such as hours of working or of consulting. No surgeries on Sundays and similar conditions. You may be able to have these conditions lifted, after a time, or you could appeal to the Secretary of State. One of my favourite conditions, and quite common for branch premises, can be 'No animals to be kept in overnight, except in an emergency'. One practice I know had this condition and, very diligently, asked the planners what they construed as an emergency. Their response was 'That would be a clinical decision for a veterinary surgeon'. Isn't it funny how many emergency admissions you can have?

Granting planning consent does not mean you can ring the builder and get stuck in with your hard hat, yellow jacket and steel toe-capped boots. There is another hurdle to pass, the Building Regulations.

Building Regulations approval

While a planning application is a review of the concept of a building, extension or change of use, it does not state that the building presented will comply with modern construction requirements. This is the role of a Building Regulations application to the building control officer, normally within the same planning department.

With a domestic premises or house extension, you can get a builder in as soon as planning consent has been received. The builder will send the building control department a notice of when work is to commence and will have to notify them at various stages of the building process, so that an inspector can visit and approve the work. The stages include foundations, damp course and so forth. This approach is not permissible for commercial premises.

Over the years the construction standards demanded for buildings within Britain have risen steadily, particularly in terms of foundations, fire prevention and escape, thermal insulation and sound travel. In fact, at times, the changing requirements can be quite complex. An example of this would link back to one standard condition of planning consent which states that the building work must be started within five years. If Building Regulations approval was given at the time of the planning application and the regulations changed before construction, the old rules still apply, i.e. you could build to out-of-date standards. Building Regulations look at the specification of the building and not the concept. This is the detailed design stage and is a relatively costly process. While it is possible to apply for both consents at the same time, or begin detailed design once the planning application is lodged, there is a financial risk should the planning application be refused. In the majority of cases it is advisable to wait until planning consent is secured before proceeding with Building Regulations approval. This is unless there are pressing reasons to take the risk or the chance of refusal is remote.

Professional advisers

Before discussing design further it may be useful to try to unravel the range of professional advisers involved in the process. There is a complex array of professions which can become involved in the construction industry, from design to completion, from architects to a range of surveyors and structural engineers. Perhaps, in fairness, I should begin with the role that I, and others of my ilk, play.

I first became involved in veterinary practice design by what I can only describe as a lucky accident. I have long been interested in buildings and design and, in my days in the veterinary pharmaceutical industry, always took an interest in new practice developments but purely from an external view. When I left the safe haven of the pharmaceutical industry, my intention was to use my marketing expertise and my membership of the Chartered Institute of Marketing, to promote better marketing and client services to the veterinary profession. I began to promote myself and, to my surprise, one of my very first calls was from a practice I had dealt with, off and on, for many years. 'Jim, I have had this mailing from you offering an external – no holds barred – review of my practice. We are thinking of redoing our reception and waiting area. You've been in more practices than I, could you come and give me some ideas?' That was in 1986. A little later it was 'I've been looking at various options for doing up my practice and was given your name by ......'

Although it was quite obvious if I had only stopped to think about it, the veterinary profession in general has little experience in building and practice design. The building professions know little about veterinary practice. I was able to use my knowledge and, more importantly, understanding of the veterinary profession to create a layout that worked effectively.

The above summary of my beginnings helps to highlight a problem of the specialist nature of veterinary practice and practice design. A well-planned veterinary practice is not a building but a vehicle for a number of specific journeys. There is

❏ the journey the client takes to the clinic and home again
❏ the journey the animal takes from home, to the clinic, and possibly through surgery, before returning home
❏ the journey the vet takes from the consulting room to the dispensary, from the theatre to the wards, the laboratory or whatever
❏ there are also the countless journeys of nurses, receptionists and all other employees within the building.

In fact the building must be an efficient and pleasant machine, designed to meet the requirements of all the users, of whatever species or standing. Trying to brief a member of the building profession about the veterinary premises machine is extremely difficult, without handing them a design from which to work. Even then there is a need to listen to, but control, their design enthusiasms if the project is to succeed within a sustainable budget.

The words 'veterinary surgeon' are clearly understood. Within the UK, they are defined as a member of the Royal College of Veterinary Surgeons. One title, one qualification, but with a range of subtleties. I can make the colour drain from the faces of some small animal vets I know, when I suggest that they may be called on to deal with a cow or a horse. They all, however, come with MRCVS after their name except, with respect, the Fellows.

The professions in the construction industry are far more wide ranging with titles such as architect, civil engineer, chartered surveyor, structural engineer, quantity surveyor, and so on, ad infinitum. When it comes to building design, most people think of architects. They are, in effect, the pinnacle of building design and, like the veterinary surgeon, their title is protected in law. As with most professions based on private practice there is an enormous range, from the journeyman architects working on domestic projects and extensions to the high profile names working on the cutting edge of design and swaying bridges. The role of an architect should be to take a brief from a client and turn it into reality within a budget. The difficulty can be the limits of the briefing and the knowledge and understanding of veterinary working procedures and movements. Most architects are supported by architectural technicians and, nowadays, CAD operators, who turn the brief into a design with the architect overseeing the process. Like most building design professions they tend to work on a percentage of the finished building costs, so their incentive to reduce costs is minimal, within the maximum possible budget. Some, now, work on fixed fees which are often based on a percentage of the expected building cost.

The widest ranging, and most confusing, of all the titles within the building profession is the term 'chartered surveyor'. The various groupings within the profession have merged, but with distinct variations. At one end are the rural surveyors, formerly known as land agents, who tend to manage farming estates and rural land. Chartered surveyor also covers many estate agents, and those who survey buildings, either for valuation or condition. There are, however, many who are involved in building design and construction management. They work almost as architects, particularly on commercial projects and alterations.

As a veterinary practice designer, I concentrate on the internal layout, links between rooms, surface finishes and certain installations. This may include the specification of flooring materials or options and details on critical dimensions. I do not, at least in detail, get involved in the structural design. That is the role of the architect or chartered surveyor.

At times, when we are suggesting a large span across a particular area, we may suggest certain approaches to the architect or surveyor responsible, but only as a nudge in the right direction. This is, in part, because we do not have the construction experience, or, more exactly, the insurance cover, to detail these aspects. One day, who knows, we may. Often, we are co-ordinating solicitors, estate agents, banks and the practice partners, as well as overseeing the progress of turning our design, or rather our client's dream, into reality.

Where projects are being undertaken at great distances, we need someone who can be on hand to manage the actual construction phase on a routine basis, sorting out queries from the contractor, or giving them a kick if the project looks to be running late. Attendance at routine site meetings would not be practical in all cases, so we limit distant visits to critical meetings. Linking with a local architect or surveyor has certain advantages, as they will know the good, and not so good, contractors, and may have useful relationships with the local planners. Whilst we normally submit the planning application, this may well be with advice from local professionals. Our aim is to gain planning consent for our client, so we do not have any concerns about upsetting a local planning officer if we have to lobby on the client's behalf. A local professional may be concerned about longer term working relationships.

When it comes to building cost estimates the main profession is the quantity surveyor (QS). On some large projects they may be involved in on-site management and cost control. Many QSs are employed by contractors to price up tender documents. While the costs per square metre guides presented earlier are useful, if you want to get a more exact cost a QS should be involved. We tend to use a QS if the project is likely to be in excess of £120,000 or looks complex. Below that figure, the fee costs may be similar to any 'guestimate' inaccuracies or our experience balanced by their calculations. Cost control is a hugely important aspect of veterinary design projects. Any practice which involves a specialist practice designer should expect them to do their utmost to keep costs down. This is achieved by keeping control of the space being created and avoiding over-artistic approaches by the structural designer, who may be trying to make a particular statement, or by checking that the specification of finishes are not over the top. With any project going to tender, the final price will depend on the tender returns. It is, of course, embarrassing if the lowest tender comes in way over the available budgets.

Another key profession is the structural engineer. They, in many respects, concentrate on building stability and may be required to design foundations on difficult land or to calculate the size of steel joists or other structural supports on alterations or tricky situations.

Where there is land subsidence or there is concern that a building may have structural problems, it will be the structural engineer who takes the lead. In fact, where a Building Regulations application is being put forward, there may be a need to submit calculations produced by a structural engineer relating to the size and construction of particular supports.

In today's construction industry there may be other professionals with titles such as 'surveyor'. There are firms which specialise in specific aspects, such as topographical surveys, where contours and features are plotted. They may have heavy investment in clever electronic technology to speed the process and produce surveys more quickly and more cheaply than could other firms using manual techniques.

When it comes to managing a building project, the contract process is normally overseen by an architect or quantity surveyor. They are the contract managers, visiting at site meetings, or as they feel necessary in between. They, like I, would be your representatives, working on your behalf.

Tenders and developers

The planning process above is relatively standard across the whole development process. The overall approach, however, can alter depending on the particular development proposed. If you buy – subject to planning consent – a freehold or leasehold plot, or you are designing an extension, you are likely to engage your own designer and other professionals. In such a situation it will be up to you whether you plump for a particular builder or go out to tender. Alternatively, you may be in the hands of a developer who owns the land and will design and build your premises. There may be no alternative than to use their construction designers and building firm, which may mean you have no competitive input on the final price. The developer will make a margin on the land, the design and the construction, but it may be all rolled into one price. While not suggesting that this will make for a more expensive building, there is no easy comparison to be made and quality control may be difficult. Where we are involved in this type of project, we invariably run the design past our own tame QS to check that the price offered by the developer is fair.

Developing all the working drawings for the finished project and putting them out for a fixed price tender is, in the main, the preferred option. I have even known of projects where the tender list consisted of one builder, but the firm did not know that when they were putting their price forward. In general, the tender should go to four or six firms which have been chosen as being capable of doing the job. This selection is important. A small, friendly, local firm may be great for repair and maintenance jobs or smaller extensions. Can they act as main contractor on a new veterinary premises, with contract floorers, piped gases and all the funding through the building process? Where you wish to add your favourite builder to the tender list, make them an extra, rather than one of the four or so.

Tender invitations all go out on the same day and the selected contractors have a set period in which to respond with their prices. This will be a fixed price for constructing the building as detailed in the specification. The return will normally state how soon they would be able to start after being notified that they had been awarded the contract and how long it will take them to construct.

Prime costs and provisional sums

Within the tender document, there may be some items marked 'P C'. This stands for either prime cost or provisional cost (or sum).

A provisional sum is included where the final detail has not been decided and the contractor cannot be expected to quote in the dark. Let us say that the detail of the reception desk had not been finalised and we include a P C of £3,000. All contractors will price their tender with the same sum for the un-designed reception desk. This allows a comparison of all tenders. A prime cost is an agreed price for a particular item from a preferred contractor. In the above example, this may be a shopfitter who will build that reception desk for £3,000. While the main contractor will manage the job, you are bringing in a specific firm to do a particular part of the overall job. In many projects piped gas and extraction systems will be installed by a specialist contractor and some form of P C will be used.

Contingency sum

Within any building project, there should be some level of contingency sum within the overall budget. Whether this is included in the tender or kept as a secret pocket, is a personal decision. Ten per cent of the overall project cost is a normal figure, but it may be varied upwards where the risk of unknown factors is high. As mentioned earlier, the most likely unexpected expenditure is at foundation level. An area of perfectly sound looking ground could reveal hidden secrets when a digger begins trenching. This could be an old well or area of disturbed ground, where extra foundations are required. The contingency may also be needed where an original provisional sum proves inadequate. Hopefully, by the time a project gets to the damp-course level, you know whether your contingency has been eaten into or remains as a potential saving.

Building contract

A fixed price tender will be run under some form of building contract. There are a range of standard contracts from small works upwards. The choice of which contract will be up to your advisers. The contract will be to construct the building as shown in the tender document and specification within an agreed time and at a fixed price. Construction quality will be controlled by your adviser, managing the project on your behalf.

There is an old saying 'A wise man changes his mind – a fool never'. Almost invariably, you will decide you want to make minor (please, only minor) amendments to the design. Any changes are likely to have an effect on the overall cost. Here again, the contingency comes into play. Handling these changes must be managed carefully. The earlier they are agreed probably the better. You will have employed a professional to manage the contract on your behalf. It is that contract manager who must issue the changed instructions and control the budget. Moving a doorway from one position to another will involve a saving in one place and a cost in the other. If the decision is made very early, it is likely that one will balance out the other. If, however, the walls are up and one doorway has to be bricked up and a new one cut, then there is a cost. The contract manager may want to ask the contractor to advise on the saving of one aspect and cost of the other, to force the contractor into the balancing of costs. This is all aimed at saving you money.

Stage payments and VAT

In most situations, you will be required to make staged payments through the contract period, normally at monthly intervals. You will be paying for work done to date as claimed by the contractor and agreed by the contract manager – the aim is to only pay out for work undertaken. Were the contractor to fail at any stage, you have the funds to bring in another firm to complete the development. In most contracts there is a percentage of each monthly payment retained, often five per cent. At the end of the contract when the contract manager agrees that work is completed, half of the retained amount will be paid. The remaining two and a half per cent is held back for the defects' period which is normally six months.

New buildings do change as the central heating goes on and the building dries out. This can create minor cracking, particularly at wall and ceiling joints or around plasterboard fixings. There may also be defects, not apparent at the final inspection, which come to notice over time. This final sum is to retain some hold over the contractor, to come back and put right the defects. If they do not, you have an amount which, with good fortune, will be sufficient to employ a different firm to make the corrections. Value added tax (VAT) will be payable on the stage payments but, in most cases, it can be reclaimed. It does, however, have a cashflow impact which needs to be managed.

Penalty clauses

Within the contract there is likely to be some level of penalty clause, should the contractor finish late. In effect, this is a fine for not complying with the construction time promised in the contract. As with many things in life, this is not always as simple as it seems. The level at which the penalty is set must be considered fair and justifiable in court. This means it needs to have a logical link to the likely costs being incurred by you because the contract is late finishing. It cannot be £10,000 per week if your only cost is hiring a £35 portable building for storage. In many cases, a figure of £250–500 per week may be reasonable.

If, during the building period, there have been alterations to the design or a contingency factor which delayed construction, these must be taken into account. Let us say an old pit was discovered along the line of a foundation trench. The building control officer may decide you need to redesign the foundations along that side. This may need a structural engineer to design the revised area. All will take time. This may create a two-week delay. Later you decide to ask for extra cupboards and shelving in the laboratory. These need ordering, with a two-week delay which stops the flooring contractor getting in on time, and so forth. The first could not be foreseen by the contractor so must be allowed, the second was caused by you.

The penalty clause is, in effect, a fine imposed on a contractor who fails to perform as originally agreed. Where construction is delayed because the contractor kept moving workers off the job or failed to order materials in time, the penalty is fair. Delays which, in all truth, could not be predicted should be treated with some flexibility wherever possible, although the contract manager should be pushing the contractor to catch up on lost time by bringing in extra staff.

Site meetings

Throughout the building period there will be a series of meetings on site, known as 'site meetings'. They invariably begin with a pre-contract meeting where the contractor, you and your advisers meet on site to discuss the project and make certain decisions. These may be critical factors like where the site hut and kettle will go or minor points like how, in the case of an extension, you will undertake orthopaedic surgery on a building site. Through the build project, site meetings will normally be monthly. These may become more frequent as the project nears the end.

During the development, the site is under the control of the contractor. A site manager or foreman, employed by the contractor, will supervise the process on their behalf. Unless the project is huge, your advisers will visit formally at the site meetings and in between if problems arise. Site meetings assess progress and quality, checking that work is on schedule and monitoring any delays. At the same time your adviser may undertake a valuation to agree the next stage payment.

Towards the end of the project there may be what may be termed a 'snagging meeting'. This is a process of compiling a list of all the defects the contractor needs to complete. A cracked drain cover here, a loose handle there, a missing sink plug, or a poor area of paint. With diligent contractors the list is small, with some it can run to pages. Two projects ending close together saw one contractor handed three A4 sheets of snagging items and the other, on inspection, point out to us one protruding nail. Guess which contractor was removed from our potential list and which went to the top?

The release of half the retained five per cent should occur at what is known as 'practical completion'. This is when the building is completed and all the snagging items corrected. Some contractors try to delay completing these minor snagging items until the end of the defects' period. They are stupid. Those minor defects gnaw away at client satisfaction and minor niggles can become major traumas. I would rather see a contractor allowed a little longer to finish off these items before the practical completion is agreed – the incentive being the two and a half percent of the whole project cost which will be released at practical completion. Any such arrangement should, however, be agreed at the start of the contract. If the contractors say the process will take 26 weeks, say 'OK: you say 26 weeks, we will give you 28, but practical completion will be when all snagging items have been sorted out, and not before'.

Whatever the contractor, at the end of the project a fully complete, high-quality building should be handed over which will serve the practice for decades to come. It can be a fraught and traumatic period, particularly if it is an extension and you are seeing the construction process in the raw for the first time. While you may be delighted with

Table 3	Typical building schedule	
Stage	**Activity**	**Time in weeks**
Site assessment	Take brief from veterinary client. Meet local planners to see if they have any major problems. Discuss highways implications. Measure site.	2
Agree layout	Prepare pencil drafts of layout for approval by client. Estimate building costs and research planning issues. Select and brief structural designer.	4
Elevations	Prepare elevation drawings. Informal meeting with planners to discuss design.	2
Prepare application	Prepare planning application and statement to counter likely objections.	2
Planning application	Begin tracking progress after four to five weeks.	8
Working drawings	Prepare working drawings for tender and Building Regulations.	4
Tender	Send tendering information to selected contractors and wait for reply.	4
Build period	Projects often begin some two weeks after the tendering process as long as all the consents have been achieved.	26
Total		52

your new development, you will probably miss the activity, site meetings and friendships you made during the construction. It can seem a bittersweet ending but at least you have your dream completed.

Time scales

From the design stage right through to turning the key on your new development can take a great deal of time. There will be set periods, like the eight-week planning process, which may become extended. Tendering is a fairly standard time but even then contractors may ask for an extended period to complete their returns. Other factors, like the construction period, will depend on the complexity and scale of the project.

Table 3 is based on a time schedule prepared for the development of new premises. In this particular case the project went as planned and the timescale proved accurate.

Section Two

Small Animal Facilities

5

Front of House

Client access and entrances
Cars and car parks

It is a fact of life that the vast majority of clients will arrive at your veterinary premises by car. This may be their own or a neighbour's or they may use a taxi. A small and declining number use public transport and a few locals may walk. The car is, without doubt, one of the greatest factors to be considered in practice planning.

You, your staff, and over time, your bonded clients will know the layout of your site and how to find their way from the car park to the entrance. Some practices do seem to make it difficult by placing the entrance in some obscure corner, up an alley or round the back. Very many clients are, thankfully for them, infrequent visitors. This does not mean they are not bonded, it just means they have, or think they have, fit and healthy animals. Just because they found their way from the car park to the door last time does not mean that they will remember this time. The point being made is that you want to make it as easy and obvious as possible for a client to come in and part with some money. The easier it is to find the entrance to the premises the better, whether that is from the other side of town or from your own car park. Where the site allows the entrance should be obvious from the frontage. Where the car park and entry point is not on the same side or not obvious, invest in some really good signs.

Accessibility in modern terms means access for all. Car parks will need a wider space near the entrance for the disabled. Where level access is not available entrances will need ramps and doorways will need to be placed so that wheelchairs can pass through and turn. These points are all set out in the Building Regulations, which are upgraded over time. Such regulations may seen an added burden and in some ways they are. A ramp for a wheelchair, however, provides easier access for a geriatric dog with matching owner and can be quite an advantage if your competition has poor accessibility.

Most planning authorities, normally district or borough councils, have set formulae which are applied to parking requirements for new premises. Veterinary premises are often linked in with health centres or group medical practices, with a formula based on staff and consulting rooms. The formulas vary around the country, but often state something like:

1	space per vet
½–1	space per lay staff member
3	spaces per consulting room (if an appointment system is used)
4	if open surgeries.

Often a planning application will need to show the layout of the car park, with room for manoeuvring and vehicles entering and leaving in a forward motion, i.e. not backing out onto the road.

Veterinary clients that tell me there is good on-street parking outside their premises often fail to see the joke when I say 'that can be cured with a can of yellow paint'. The local highways department can be the greatest threat to practice profitability. Having control of client access and parking is a huge advantage for a veterinary practice, making it easy for clients to call and reducing the muttering from neighbours.

Following a car journey most dogs have a desire to relieve themselves fairly promptly. (I am sure we have all been driven by people who can create a similar effect.) It follows that street parking around a surgery creates a mess, adding a second area for complaints from neighbours. A practice car park can, therefore, stop two of the major areas of conflict with the locals. The practice must, however, recognise that dogs will still need to relieve themselves and this aspect of patient behaviour should be managed. Regular poop-scoop patrols and a doggy toilet area are good approaches. Bags and dog-mess bins would also help. Signs saying 'Do not let dogs foul the area' are not very welcoming and can give out a hugely negative message. Dogs which relieve themselves in the car park or doggy loo area may refrain from cocking their leg on the doorpost or diet display.

The entrance

The client entrance door, as mentioned earlier, should be obvious and logically positioned. There are other factors which need consideration relating to the entrance such as people movements, animal security and dirt control. With ten-minute consultations, each consulting room should create six inward and six outward door openings per hour, if fully

booked. Just think how many times per day the entrance is likely to be used. There is an obvious need for a good quality door which can stand the workload. In wet, cold weather each inward movement will bring at least two wet feet and normally more. Each will bring an icy blast to chill the waiting room and the receptionist. Wet floors can be slippery and dangerous and the area can become a mud bath very quickly. Apart from the unsightly appearance the wet and grime will damage the flooring, causing it to wear more quickly.

To block the cold blast, having two doorways for the client to pass through is a great advantage. It will, also, reduce the risk of animal escape and create a lobby. This lobby should be a dirt barrier. With the correct floor surface it can clean the feet and reduce dirt and wet being trailed onto your pristine waiting room floor. This is particularly important if slip-resistant flooring is being used in the waiting room. The floor surface that grips the feet, to reduce slipping by clients and their skating dogs, also grips grime.

There is a range of options for flooring a barrier area. Old-fashioned coir (coconut) matting is low cost and highly effective. Nowadays it comes with rubber backing and can be cut and fitted to size. Coir matting is, however, difficult to clean particularly if the lobby area is quite small. Larger areas, say with two sets of double doors some two metres apart, seem to have little difficulty. Moving away from coir there are many alternatives. These include ribbed rubber strips, as sometimes seen in department store entrances or routinely laundered contract barrier mats. The laundered mats are increasingly popular. They lay flat on the floor with a carpet-type finish in the centre and a rubber edge some 50–75 mm wide. They are also ideal where no lobby exists, but they do require a continuing laundry contract to keep them working effectively.

All barrier areas need special management and regular cleaning. Door posts can become leg-cock stops and, if a scent is allowed to build, the popularity of the posts increases. Whatever the barrier flooring, the area needs ventilation and routine deodorising if the client's first impression is not to be a scent of urine.

Over the barrier you hope to keep the floor as clean and dry as possible, though some dirt will get across, particularly in very wet weather. When choosing the colour of your floor covering, remember most dirt dries so much lighter than you would think. Dark floors, like dark coloured cars, are a pain to keep looking clean. If in doubt, go lighter. On one of our earliest new-build projects, the client chose a floor colour that was almost white. I had tried to suggest something a little darker but the client knew what they wanted and, to be fair, have proved that most mud dries just off-white. Their floor always looks great.

As a child, visits to the vet were quite rare. My lasting impression, decades on, remains the quarry-tiled floor, polished to an unnatural red with 'Cardinal Polish'. I have never seen dogs slide around and do the splits like it! Highly polished floors are not good for dogs, infirm clients or insurance premiums. Whether it is my childhood memories or just logic, I fight against them at every step.

Before we move in let us retrace our steps a little and consider the more ephemeral points of entering a veterinary premises. What is it like inside? Is it busy? Is there a nasty dog – just coming out? Being able

PARVO
VIRUS
KILLS

to see
inside before
you enter reduces any potential anxiety. Being
able to see a light, bright and spacious interior is encouraging and
removes the unknown. This may be achieved by large windows or
doors with glass panels top and bottom.

Where visibility through the door is good there is less risk of two
opposing dogs having a go at each other in the doorway. While it could
bring work, it is rather poor client relations. An alternative would be to
have separate doors, 'in' and 'out'. These should be relatively close
together to avoid confusion, and certainly not a complete one-way system. There are horror stories of people having to do a lap of honour to
collect family members left in the waiting room.

Reception and waiting areas

While every practice strives to gain bonded clients, many people coming through the door will be infrequent visitors or new clients. These
are the people we must cater for. The bonded clients will have become
familiar with the experience of visiting your premises.

As a less familiar client enters the premises their senses will be
heightened. They will experience the sights, sounds and smells which
face all who venture inside. Take a moment to think of a time when you
walked into an unfamiliar place; you see the wear and tear, grubby areas

and sense the odd odours. If, however, the place is clean, pleasant and odour free, your senses seem to note those facts but ignore them. You feel more comfortable with the surroundings and your senses calm. It is always useful for senior veterinary practice staff to enter by the client door, at least now and then, to monitor the experience. We frequently get calls when a partner returns from holidays and senses the places afresh or rather not so fresh! For many veterinary surgeons, front-of-house is foreign territory. They have never tried to work reception but think they can plan it, and have never tried to deal with the client just entering their premises or faced with the bill.

Many writers on the subject suggest that around one quarter of the total ground floor area should be used for reception and waiting. That is a little like seven human years being the equivalent to one dog year. It can be a useful tool for getting a point across but cannot be considered as a scientific fact. Practices which want to run open surgeries will need more client handling space than those with efficient appointment systems. Those intent on high levels of product sales need more space than those which do not.

What is required, if at all possible, is a light, bright, airy space where people can wait in comfort without constant concern that their dog will be in a fight or their cat consumed by a dog. I once visited a practice in north-east England, in the heart of Greyhound country. They ran separate clinics for Greyhounds and I asked why. 'We used to lose the odd rabbit in open surgery' was the serious reply.

Reception desk

In terms of layout the position of reception is a major factor in calming clients. If, when walking through the door, the 'check-in' is obvious, the calming process continues. All too often otherwise well-designed premises are let down by the reception desk creating a bottleneck just inside the door or being tucked away out of sight.

Clients are not just people, but people with animals. While someone with a cat in a carrier may not take up much space, someone with a large dog on a lead does. If that dog is a bit grizzly or of a breed that sparks caution, other clients tend to want to give it a wide berth.

Over the years there have been a number of differing approaches to the design and positioning of reception desks. In the 1980s some practices installed the reception as an island unit in the middle of the waiting area. Such a design, in my view, shows a complete lack of understanding about the role and duties of a receptionist and the isolation they can feel. Sadly, in this day and age, they may be faced with quite threatening situations, like the potentially violent client or someone interested in the contents of the till. Placing them in a central bear-pit is hardly fair.

The work of the receptionist can vary quite considerably from one practice to another. Sometimes the role is purely receiving clients and, following their visit, dealing with the account. Most, in fact, also handle telephone calls and many hand over medication or even dispense. The size, design and layout of the reception desk will depend on the client throughput and the roles undertaken. This is particularly true on the side of the desk where the receptionist works which we will discuss later.

Clients visit the reception point standing. You want them to sign consent forms, cheques and credit card slips. It follows that the height should serve that purpose. This higher level also provides a rather useful barrier which, hopefully rarely, may be a valuable safety feature. One potential problem with high reception desks is that you may not notice a very small person or child wanting to be served and you would not be able to deal professionally with someone in a wheelchair. As modern planning regulations insist on disabled access and service this point does need consideration. Some lower area away from the main

service points can be useful. You probably do not want clients to plonk down their cat carrier or dog on the counter surface. The easiest way to stop this is to have that top quite narrow, and ask politely. I have seen tops with a slight slope but that could cause problems. Writing a cheque, holding a handbag and a strong dog, is not easy. Placing hooks for bags and leads is a nice touch as long as the desk is well anchored and the hooks will not catch clothing.

On the business side of the counter, there are likely to be computers, telephones, a credit card machine, a money drawer or till, and various other items of technology. Receptionists will need to handle paper-work, handouts, consent forms and leaflets. All this technology and paper needs storing, and it often changes. This type of work is best done seated, so the work-side should be of desk height. A fully fitted area designed for today may need a refit quite soon if it is not to become difficult to work. A more creative approach may be to design in adapt-ability with movable units, paper trays and the like under the desk surface. Many such items are easily purchased from office suppliers and are far cheaper than a fully-fitted design which may be outdated in a few years.

Sales areas

Sales areas are of increasing importance in many practices. Often the approach is to use stands supplied by the product manufacturers, which may not be the best use of space. These units, after all, are designed to display their products rather than fit in your waiting room.

Shops load their prices to take account of thefts, with the quaint phrase 'stock shrinkage'. Small and easily pocketed items can walk out of the door, some with quite high values and relatively low margins. Having the sales area close to reception does increase supervision and make it easier for the receptionist to discuss products with clients.

Space costs money and careful thought should be given to the likely return of each square metre of floor space dedicated to selling products where the margins are not very large. Major retailers charge the prod-ucts on the shelf rent, or use some similar costing formula to decide which products are allowed in prime space. There is a fine line between a veterinary practice selling some useful, veterinary-endorsed products and diets, and a pet shop with a vet behind. Where that line actually sits is difficult to assess and in many respects is constantly moving. One of the most attractive approaches is to have a specially fitted sales area close to, but not hindering, reception. This can be well lit and branded with the practice name and logo, adding consistency to the image.

Waiting areas

Many people have tried the idea of separate waiting areas for dogs and cats. In principle it is a good idea but there are some real problems which make it less practical. What do you do with the client who brings a cat and a dog? How many stroppy dogs to you want in one area?

Wherever possible a practical alternative is to create seating bays in the waiting area. One can be reserved for cats only, either using signage or by presenting cat care information and images on the wall. Other seating bays allow people to sit in different areas, avoiding clients and patients of concern. In fact, the more seating bays the better, as long as the reception desk has full visual supervision over the entire area where clients are unattended.

A number of veterinary practices have tried to have child-friendly areas. This is a nice touch, but one which must be approached with care. I worry when visiting our GP that the kids might pick up something nasty from the soft toys available for play. In a veterinary practice, there is a point of avoiding small items which could cause choking – not only for the child, but by a patient. Animal stories, animal pictures to colour and similar distractions could be applicable. Toys should be large enough and made of strong, cleanable materials. Furthermore, someone should manage the area.

Client information

While waiting times should be as brief as possible, there is a chance of influencing and educating clients. Wall panels, notice boards and leaflets, if well presented and managed, can be very valuable. Other waiting room entertainment, like video players and moving signs, may be wanted. These should be considered at the planning stage as power will be required.

Sound deadening

A large open area surrounded by hard surfaces can sound a little like a works canteen on Christmas party night. Reducing sound travel is quite difficult to achieve but seating bays and strategically placed bulkheads can help, along with softer seating squabs, plants and similar barriers. The most important area for sound deadening is between the waiting area and consulting room. You do not want waiting clients to hear too many yelps or sobs from inside and the client is unlikely to grasp what you say if there are 'noises off'.

Keeping a clear area in front of the consulting room doors is a useful factor which, combined with well-fitted solid doors, will help. Any vents required for the consulting room should not come from the waiting area, but from the back or sides of the building. If the waiting has been pleasant and not too long, the client may enter the consulting room in a calm and friendly state of mind. Well, we live in hope.

The consulting room

The consulting room is where heightened anxiety meets cool, calm professionalism. In most cases it should be the client whose tension is raised. For the clients, entering into the consulting room represents a move from the public forum to the inner sanctum. The experience of the waiting room is left behind as the private consultation, the process for which they are paying, finally gets under way.

In a busy surgery with ten-minute appointments there is a danger that one single consultation is just another segment of a fully booked session. The vet in familiar surroundings tries to sort out the problems of another punter's pet who is on potentially hostile ground. In the period from the consulting room door opening for a client to enter, to it closing as they depart, veterinary reputations are made and lost. It is, without doubt, the core aspect of the out-patient service.

The consulting room must satisfy the needs of the client, the consulting veterinarian and the animal patient like no other part of the premises. The overall experience must be satisfactory to all three parties if the work space is to be effective.

There are certain logistics which need consideration in relation to the entry, harbouring and exit of the client. The way in which the door opens will determine how the client enters and where they end up. That client may, in fact, be accompanied. Some consultations may involve several family members bringing one or more patients so the size of the room can be an important factor in the equation.

In most consulting rooms the examination table is used as a partial barrier across the room. This divides the space into a client area which the vet tries not to enter, a vet area where the client is not allowed, and the patient as the centre of attention. The consulting table acts as a barrier similar to the desk of a corporate mogul – boss on one side, minion on the other. This point is not a criticism, more a statement of fact. Sticking to this division can, however, limit the workings of the space and the level of client satisfaction. For the time being, it serves our purpose to consider these three specific areas of a consulting room: client, patient and vet.

Client area

The client area must be of sufficient size to cater for the normal maximum family. I well remember developing one of our first new-build practices where budgets were extremely tight. Despite all the planning and calculations, the initial building quotations told us that we had to save space. As luck would have it, we held what amounted to a premises' obesity clinic in the home of my client. This had a good-sized kitchen with a quarry-tiled floor. After much debate we decided to role play consulting in the kitchen, using a piece of chalk and the quarry tiles on the floor as a guide. As the new building rose from the ground and the dark grey block walls of the consulting rooms took shape, my heart began to sink. Plaster and paint seemed to make the spaces larger, but not all that much.

One week after the new surgery opened I received a call from my client. There was clear relief in his voice: 'It's passed the Glover test'. Not wanting to sound too ignorant about the intricacies of veterinary practice I waited for further explanation. The Glovers, it turned out, were a family of four, each weighing in as a heavyweight, who insisted on accompanying their, thankfully, small dog into the consulting room. Only then did I realise that my anxiety about the size of the consulting rooms was shared by my client.

During a consultation, the client may be asked or wish to become involved in holding the patient while the examination or treatment takes place. This may lead to a client wanting to wash their hands, so client access to the hand basin is useful. The positioning of that basin will have a marked effect on the accessibility to both client and vet.

Veterinary area

All the major activities within the consulting room take place around the examination table or in the area dominated by the consulting vet. This is the area where all the services need to be located if the area is to work well in terms of ergonomics and logistics.

As the years pass there seem to be more and more gadgets which need to be plugged into the electricity supply in the consulting room. Computers, printers, auroscopes, X-ray viewers, special lights and mains chargeable this and that. All these items are required in the vet area, none in the client area. Apart from, perhaps, a single socket for the cleaner to plug into, all the power supply needs to be in the veterinary surgeon's area. One approach which seems to work well is to count the maximum likely appliances to be plugged in and supply each with a double socket, leaving half spare for the gadgets of the next decade. This may be best achieved by using an electrical dado ducting, where sockets can be added or moved should need arise.

At present the most bulky piece of electrical equipment in the consulting room is the computer, particularly the screen. Over the next few years flat screen technology, or rather pricing, may consign this piece of kit to a small area of the wall. Until such time the computer terminal takes up a valuable amount of space, often just where you would rather have something else. Moreover, a computer VDU comes with a keyboard and, possibly, a mouse, all taking up valuable space. A good approach to housing a computer and keyboard within a consulting room is to have the VDU on one pivoting wall bracket, and the keyboard and mouse on another. This allows the VDU to be turned in any direction, to show or not to show, and for the keyboard to be adjusted for any operator, left or right handed. Both, ideally, should be positioned for comfortable use while standing.

Over recent years a number of factors have led us to adjust the design of consulting rooms. These relate to computers, medicines' legislation, storage and the linkage of different work spaces. The early hospital regulations required running water either in the consulting room or close by, say, in a shared dispensary passage. Today the requirement is for a hand basin or sink, with hot and cold water, in each consulting room. Our current approach is to position the hand basin so that both vet and client have access without a dance around the area, and to separate basin from computer by as much space as can be achieved.

With a shared medicine and stock passage running behind the consulting room there should be no need for any storage in the consulting room. This in turn removes the argument for a sink and full depth worktop running across the back of the room; a potential saving of 600 mm on the room dimensions, front to back. This, of course, is a matter of choice but can help keep within a tight budget.

Although it takes some discipline, confining all stock to a storage passage greatly reduces overall stock holdings and helps keep the practice within the letter and spirit of the Medicines Act. As legislation evolves this is likely to become a much more significant factor.

Patient area

At last we come to the most important area in terms of clinical practice, that space occupied by the patient. A consulting table is often located like a peninsula unit, narrow end on to a wall or situated as a partial barrier across the centre of the room. Perched high in the air is the patient, quivering with fear at the altitude. Such a position is fine for the smaller dog, cat and many other patients. For many, however, it is an unnerving position, although the fear factor may add to compliance. I have never been privy to the inside knowledge of how the little old lady with the obese Labrador elevates her charge to that lofty height or, for 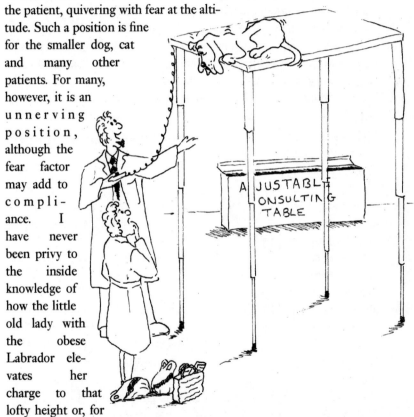 that matter, returns it, quaking to earth. I do, however, know many vets who have a regular appointment with an osteopath.

Sometime in 1979, I visited an ageing veterinary surgeon who was a sole practitioner in outback Lincolnshire. I was ushered in to meet the vet who was in the process of spaying a giant-sized St Bernard...on the floor. There, squatting on the floor, was the veterinary surgeon. Having pre-medicated the dog, there was no way that he and his receptionist could lift it onto the operating table. All, including the vet, are believed to have recovered completely.

The point I am trying to make is that one size does not fit everyone. Often that examination table is more of a hindrance than a benefit and needs to be moved aside or not used, if patient and client are to receive satisfactory attention. Where the consulting room is large, the examination table may be ignored for large dogs. In other situations, it may be useful to push it to one side, out of the way. The alternative is to install a wall-mounted, fold-down unit which can be folded back to create extra floor-space, as required.

When it comes to the overall size of an individual consulting room, much will depend on the preference of the practice and the budget. Large consulting rooms can look splendid but be tiring to work in, moving from the central examination table to various parts of the room to collect items required. Much will depend on the space the vets are

Figure 2   Consulting room layout 1

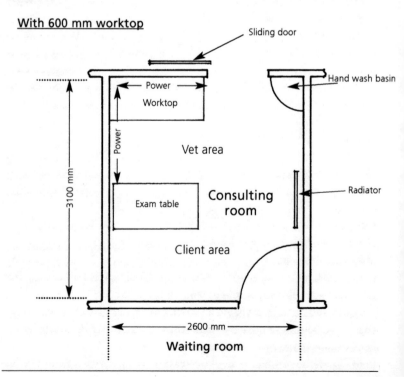

accustomed to using in the past. Often with new-build projects we can develop a good working environment in an area of 2.6 m (8′ 6″) wide by 2.6 m (8′ 6″) to 3.0 m (9′ 10″) front to back. While these dimensions are subject to the equipment within, they are our comfortable minimum. This is not to say we have not created smaller consulting rooms, but not usually on new-build premises.

In order to achieve a comfortable working environment, light and ventilation are vital factors. While many may prefer natural light, this can be difficult to achieve in all consulting rooms using traditional design approaches. Living without natural light in a consulting room is not normally a problem as long as the artificial lighting is sufficiently bright without harsh shadows. Windows, in some respects, can be more of a problem than a benefit. If the room is positioned where the sun can stream in at certain times, consulting may be difficult. Furthermore, there is a risk of patient escape if windows are opened for ventilation. Good ventilation is essential in all consulting rooms. Many practices now opt for air conditioning as the goal, but the key is frequent air changes and the opportunity to boost airflow to help remove any odours. This is true whether there is natural light or not.

With ventilation comes fans, whether in an air conditioning unit or otherwise. Fans bring with them the risk of noise, possibly making it difficult to listen to certain body sounds. In all cases it is good to have the quietest practical ventilation but to be able to switch it off, briefly, if required. The art is to remember to switch it back on again.

Consulting room layout

The consulting room layout in Figure 2 shows a basic layout covering the points mentioned earlier. The position of the hand basin or small sink avoids contact between water and electricity, as well as providing easy access to both the consulting vet and the client.

All doors used should be of solid construction to reduce sound travel. Cheap hollow doors have minimal sound deadening, so limit the privacy of a consultation. Depending on the layout and space available there is a choice to be made relating to the door between the consulting room and rear passageway. Hinged doors can be a real nuisance unless there is a good deal of space. Sliding doors, however, must run on very high quality tracks as they may be opened and closed up to 20,000 times per year.

The decision relating to the positioning of equipment used within the consulting room must be left to discussion within the practice. If, say, an X-ray viewer is to be installed, should it be close to the consulting table so that an X-ray can be shown to the short-sighted client while their animal remains held on the table, or across the room possibly above the position shown for the radiator?

The layout in Figure 3 does not show a computer or any shelving. If pivot brackets are used the best position for the computer is on the side wall, behind the consulting table. The screen can then be turned either way, so it can be shown to the client or concealed. While some shelving will be required this should be kept to a minimum, otherwise clutter will begin to build and the room look untidy, possibly unclean. Whether or not there is a radiator in the consulting room will depend on the heating system chosen. Radiators are not ideal; they are low-cost and reliable, but they do get hot. The position shown is probably the safest for all concerned, and away from most accidental contact. Some form of enclosed guard may be of value to stop client and patient contact.

Figure 3   Consulting room layout 2

<u>Without 600 mm worktop</u>

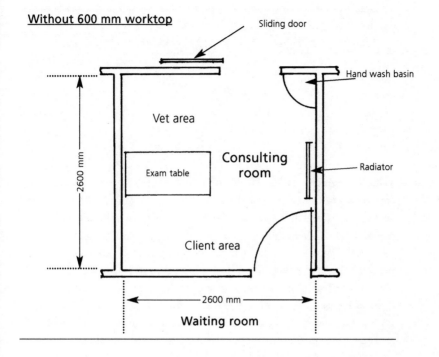

6

In-House Services

Dispensaries and practice supplies

Before we become embroiled in the design aspects of a practice dispensary, it is worth reviewing the range of supplies which end up in there. This will help decide the types of storage required and the space needed to house the various product groupings. If we consider how the products leave the dispensary and where they are distributed, we will start to realise that different practices have differing requirements depending on their working practices and work range. There is an important review process which is needed so that any designer can arrange storage to suit practice needs. Most UK veterinary practices purchase a higher proportion of their supplies from the wholesale network. The range of products goes far beyond licensed medicines, dressings and other items which will be directly associated with medical treatments. All must be ordered, delivered, checked-off and logged into storage. With good stock control and daily wholesale deliveries the average storage period should not be very long. It follows, therefore, that the overall storage space required should not need to be too great, if well organised.

Whatever the range of products arriving in a delivery, they create an immediate logistical problem by taking up space while they are checked off and put away. In terms of practice design there is a need for a designated point to receive supplies and sufficient space to accommodate the delivery until it is moved into storage.

During the Falklands' War, Brian Hanrahan became famous for informing the British public that none of the aircrew crew were missing on a sortie from an aircraft carrier. He was controlled by reporting restrictions but made the point by saying 'I counted them off and I counted them back'. This is the very essence of stock control and, as profit margins on medicines begin to fall, one which is essential to learn.

A very good management tool is to have some form of central stock store, where all products are placed and from where all movements are traced. In some ways, this is your own internal wholesaler. From this store, which we may call the dispensary, product movements are recorded and traced whether they leave as part of a prescription or go to the preparation area for in-patient treatment.

Figure 4   **Medical supplies flowchart**

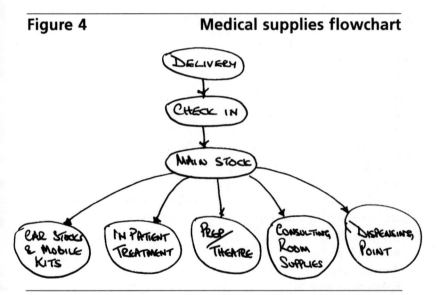

In order to maintain a good control system, it is wise to hold only complete, unopened packs within the main stock room. Products to be dispensed from bulk should be moved to a designated dispensing area where separate controls can be maintained. In print this may sound somewhat bureaucratic; the dispensary area could be within the same air space – just separate and distinct. This will help keep control.

Back in the 1980s I remember a call from a vet I knew well. He was clearly concerned about his stock control system and tried to explain the situation. 'On average' he began 'we buy around £20,000 of medicines per month and maintain a steady stock holding. Having looked at the last three months, we are selling an average of £20,000 per month.'

Figure 5

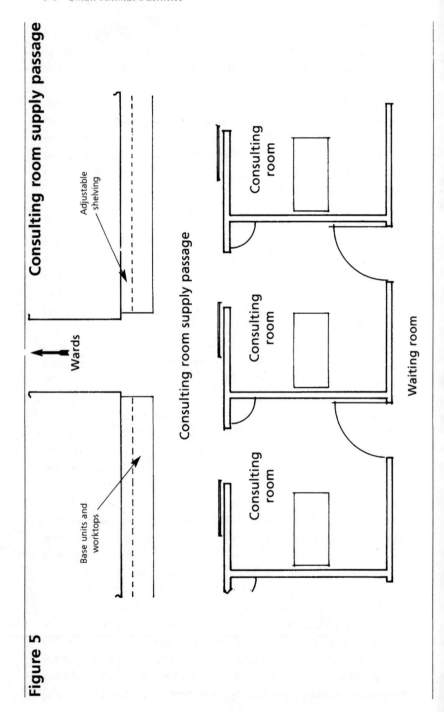

Consulting room supply passage

'What's the problem?' I asked.

'Problem! Problem!' he exploded 'We have a 50% mark up!'

Apart from dressings and other items consumed in the practice which were not being charged out, the main problem was vets leaving products on farms and not booking them down. The creation of a central stock room and tighter control on car boots, soon brought the problem more under control. The flowchart presented earlier shows the ways in which medicines move from the main dispensary. In terms of the design of a veterinary premises, we can ignore 'vet's stock' and concentrate on other usage areas.

Consulting room supplies

I am a great fan of the layout where the consulting rooms are supplied by a connecting passage which used to be called a 'dispensary passage'. We dropped this term in late 2000 when the Marsh Committee was established. We now think of it as the 'consulting room supply passage' to distinguish the area from the dispensary which may be where prescribed medicines are dispensed.

Holding stock of medicines in each consulting room is hugely expensive and probably illegal. It is certainly illegal if you ever leave a client in the room while you nip out to get something. For the client the range of medicines may look colourful but they tend to make the place harder to clean and easily cluttered and there could be breakages should certain patients decide to shelf-walk.

In fact, the rear supply passage has so many advantages they are hard to list. This includes the professional admission of patients, the removal of cadavers or a secondary exit route for a distressed client. Other advantages can include a hovering nurse who can support two or three consulting vets, a mini-library for rapid reference and a contact link to reception. As the need to separate prescribing and dispensing dawns, a shared supply passage, linked to a prescription dispensing area and the main store should satisfy all concerned.

In-patient housing

The housing of in-patients could be the subject of a volume on its own. This could range over the housing requirements of all the different species, pre-op/post-op, medical cases, intensive care, long-stay, the provision of exercise and so forth. For this section the approach will concentrate on design and consider the location within the premises together with some factors associated with different broad groupings.

Today most in-patients are admitted and discharged either via a consulting room or a dedicated nurse's room. While a nurse's room may have different fitments and may need to be slightly larger, it is wise to link this to the supply passage like an extra consulting room. There is a logic in having in-patient housing within easy reach of the consulting rooms for easier admission and discharge. At the same time, however, you do not want a consultation to be disturbed by the sound of a dog howling its way out of an anaesthetic.

Another factor in the equation is the practice approach, now and in the future, to in-patient visitors. If visitors are allowed or even welcomed, you do not want to trail through the preparation area or give them a front row seat at the new assistant's first spay. The idea of clients visiting patients comes with advanced surgical techniques, where the animal may need to be hospitalised for some time. There can be concerns that a visit from the owner may be disturbing to the patient or other in-patients. That is a matter for practice policy, which is a wonderful cop out. I once heard a practice manager defend their policy of permitting clients to visit their pets by saying 'It's not the animal that pays the bill'.

Of course there may be occasions when you would wish to show people around the premises. This leads to a decision about how much you are prepared to invest to separate animal housing from clinical action. A good compromise would seem to be some form of passage as a dividing line between in-patients and work areas, wards on the left, preparation on the right or vice versa.

Separate wards

The idea of separate wards for dogs and cats now seems to be a general aim and a requirement for hospital status. This approach will certainly appeal to the pet owner who would hate to think that a large angry dog is eyeballing their little kitty. A similar separation can be achieved, however, with back-to-back cage units, dogs on one side, cats on the other.

With the current trend in pet ownership extending the range of species, the concept of separation needs some review. What about rabbits, rats, and birds, not to mention hospitalised iguanas or tarantula spiders? Perhaps dogs, cats and others is the current ward compromise.

Ward layout

When considering the conversion of an existing building, animal housing is often an area where design has to be compromised. Cages, after all, can fit various ways round and sizes can be purchased or commissioned to match the space. Even with purpose-built units there may be some need for compromise, at least to keep within a reasonable budget. Many veterinary surgeons try to avoid animals facing each other across an in-patient ward, at least for dogs. This can be difficult to achieve without a long passage of a ward which may, in fact, not suit the overall layout. In fact, many practices end up with dogs facing dogs across a ward passage, at least in part of the ward. Few report any problems, as long as a disruptive dog can be moved elsewhere.

Where in-patient treatments are to be undertaken within the ward space, some examination or treatment may be required. A better arrangement may well be to have an in-patient examination room, like

a small consulting room, close to all wards.

Any passage between cages, or in any ward, must be 900–1000 mm (3'0"–3'3")wide, to permit cage doors to open to their full extent. This, backed by the fact that standard cages may be between 700 mm and 800 mm (2'3"to 2'6") deep, begins to show the space required. Where space is critical, it is vital to flag this up in building specifications, so the contractor is fully aware of the requirements. There is no compromise with the dimensions of steel cages and builders are not used to working to millimetres, or even inches, at times!

Dog ward layouts

Of all the small animal species housed, the dog presents the greatest range of size requirements; from giant breeds to ones which would not make a good snack! The logic is to have a mix of cage sizes with large ones along the base and smaller ones above. Some cage manufacturers offer a range of cage depths to suit various dogs. This has a logic, but can create a dilemma. If the base row of cages is 250 mm (10") deeper than those above, do you stack the upper cages to line with the fronts, leaving a void behind or to the back, creating a shelf to lean over to grab your patient?

Where space is unlimited, the ideal is to house small and medium dogs in a standard cages but have larger dogs in walk-in cages. Walk-in cages take up a huge amount of space and there is always need for some compromise. With stacked dog cages, two high is the practical maximum. The space above, if planned, can be used for all those extras like bedding, heat pads and other necessities. Often this 'over-cage' storage space is better planned outside a main building contact, using the practice maintenance joiner, rather than a main contractor with higher overheads and higher hourly charges.

With any cage stack, cat or dog, there is the problem of having power on hand for heat pads and other items without trailing cables around the place. In this area, cage design is sadly lacking, but the problem can be easily cured. The simple solution is to build a pelmet-type structure above the two-cage high bank, with a run of 13 amp sockets in the pelmet and cupboards above.

Walk-in cages

Walk-in cages are ideal for large dogs or where an animal is comatose and you need access all around it and, probably, the addition of drips. The difficulty is to decide how large they should be.

In a conversion project there may well be an awkward corner where standard cages would not be appropriate and a walk-in cage can be built. It is also possible to buy these items 'off the shelf' or have them designed to your requirements. Even with walk-in cages it can be useful to have a range of sizes. A floor area of 1000 mm by 1500 mm (3'3" x 4'4") may be adequate for most requirements, though several giant breeds would be hard-pressed to lie flat in that floor area.

One caring client of ours had to house a very great Great Dane overnight. The only walk-in cage was in the isolation area but still not big enough to give this gentle giant a pleasant night. Being kind our client decided to shut the dog in the X-ray room as the design gave a large clear floor area. At 3.20 a.m. he was woken by the police. The

Dane had unlatched the door and set off the alarm. The police, shining torches through opaque glass, could only see enormous eyes reflecting back at them. When our client arrived at his surgery, the police stood well back as he unlocked the door.

One great advantage about walk-in cages is that you have walls on either side. This can make it easy to have a device which supports a drip hanging at any point. If there is no top you should remember that some dogs can climb or leap extraordinary heights. With a good door height it may be worth considering some form of mesh across the top to stop the determined escaper.

Cat wards

Cats come in a much narrower range of sizes than dogs, which may be stating the obvious but does mean that housing can be more uniform. The cage sizes may be varied, depending on the length of stay envisaged or whether you are having a queen and litter. From a design point of view I often feel that practices waste space in cat wards by offering short-stay patients far more room than is really necessary, both in terms of base area and height. It may be, of course, that some cat cages may house the odd small dog – cross species isolation, and all that. The principle of a bank of cat cages holds good with some larger units along the bottom run to accommodate longer-stay patients. The difficulty is how high do we go? That, to some extent, depends on where you began!

Extracting a reluctant cat from a high cage can be a scary occupation. (There should, probably, be a risk assessment and safety policy review at this point.) It can be as bad to be on your knees, peering inside to entice a cat from the back of a floor level cage. So can the design help? Depending on the height of cages used, it is possible to go three high, particularly if you are not too generous with headroom. Almost as useful is to have the lowest tier higher off the floor. Standard practice is to have the bottom run of cages some 100 mm (4″) off the floor, seated on a plinth. This allows the flooring to have a coved finish, making for easier cleaning. Raising the height of that plinth to 250–300 mm (10–12″) will make a huge difference when trying to deal with the occupant of the lower cages.

At the opposite extreme is the top-tier cat described earlier. The biggest problem is that you may be reaching up and back with the cat flat against the rear of the cage, like a spy hiding in the shadows. In this

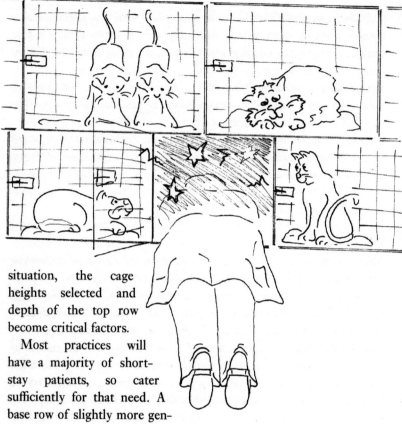

situation, the cage heights selected and depth of the top row become critical factors.

Most practices will have a majority of short-stay patients, so cater sufficiently for that need. A base row of slightly more gen-erous cages, say all 600 mm (2') high and a range of widths from 600 mm (2') with possibly one as large as 750–900 mm (2'6"–3'). The two rows above that can use lower height cages, around 450 mm (1'6") high, with the top tier having cages of reduced depth, fitted flush to the front of the cage bank.

Even with a high base plinth it should be possible to get the floor of the top cage at around 1300–1350 mm (4'3"–4'7") even if the very top is somewhat higher.

Recovery cages

One of the greatest dangers of smart, separate animal wards with care-ful segregation of species is the risk that an in-patient does not get the supervision required because it has been neatly tidied away in a ward. The recovery period is critical and does need careful monitoring.

In the good old days it was not uncommon to see a vet operating on one animal with all the earlier cases recovering on the operating theatre floor. Now and then, as you chatted about the weather, the weekend or workload, the vet would leap over and sort out a prone recoverer. Then, back to the chat and chop. While many would criticise such an approach, the recovering animals were getting close supervision. Moreover, had anyone monitored recovery losses, I would be prepared for a little wager on the results.

The management of recovering patients is a decision for the practice and it may well be that nurses can monitor recovering patients within a ward. There may, however, be a point in having some dedicated recovery cages somewhere where there is a specific supervisory function. Often this is in part of the preparation area, or close by.

Isolation

The concept of full isolation for highly infectious patients is difficult to achieve where the number of such cases is not very high. It is hard to achieve because nursing staff and duty vets may have to care for these cases along with all the others. The term 'isolation' means separation; not just of animals, but air space, body fluids, drainage and support.

Many cases requiring isolation will be picked up during a consultation and, as far as possible, should be moved away from all other in-patients. If biosecurity could be ensured, a good position would have an entrance to the consulting areas and be completely separate from all other animal housing. Such a location may be neither possible nor secure.

The isolation ward should be able to cater for the largest likely patients as well as the norm. For many practices one walk-in cage, plus a range of other sizes, would seem to the logical approach. Separating air space is easy using extractor fans drawing the air within the isolation ward out of the building. Separate drainage is also quite simple. You then come to waste and supportive functions. Within the isolation area there should be some facility for washing and cleaning. This may be a full sink or a hand-basin. There should also be room for dealing with the nursing needs of the patient, much of which will be based around the cage or kennel. Where space is difficult a normal examination table may not be appropriate, although a wall-mounted unit, which is folded down when required, would be advantageous.

For overall cleanliness and biosecurity it would be unwise to store items in the isolation room, other than possibly cleaning materials and disinfectants. All medicines and dressings should be brought in only as required.

Intensive care

When it comes to the intensive care of animal patients, there is a need to define what is required. Different practices have different approaches and, therefore, differing requirements.

As in recovery the key factor is supervision, so the location within the animal area will need careful consideration. There are the further complications of additional requirements, such as heat pads, drips, monitors and similar items, all requiring space and services.

Combining supervision and peace and quiet may be difficult though some opt for an area screened off with a glazed partition observation panel. Others opt for a particular cage, within a ward, where there is space for drips and a power supply. This is an aspect where the veterinary practice must be clear in their requirements if a satisfactory function is to be achieved.

Dog runs

Dog runs and planning authorities rarely mix well, so great care is needed in the presentation of such a requirement. In terms of location the ideal position is with direct access to the dog ward which may, or may not, be achievable. A caged compound with concrete base, drain and tap, is not difficult to construct but it may not suit all positions. If your practice premises is isolated, the idea of some dogs in runs, visible to visitors, may not be a problem – even a positive feature. Many, however, will need to plan for an enclosed yard rather than open pens.

With security in mind, it may be wise to have the only way in and out of a pen through the building, rather than having some outer gate. Again, this may not be practical if the area has to double as a fire escape route. One very practical problem is the long-stay dog that will only perform on grass. If these patients are to be satisfied with an external pen, we are talking space, escape tunnels and cleaning problems. Most practices find the only solution is a walk on a lead and a hunt for some greenery.

Cadavers, clinical and pharmaceutical waste

Few businesses can be faced with the differing disposal demands of the modern veterinary practice – from potentially contaminated water through the drainage system and invisible gases, to all things involving transportation and packaging.

One of our earliest design projects came to us because a senior partner, with something of a short fuse, had had a bust up with a long-time friend who happened to be an architect. The architect had been asked to come up with a design for a new practice premises, probably with no real brief whatsoever. Using a certain logic, the architect had positioned the mortuary next to the operating theatre and the vet had taken this as a personal attack on his surgical prowess. I must admit the vet was quite open about the reason for the fall out and, as he recounted the tale, his neck reddened and his face scowled. Imagine being the listener and trying to avoid a smile.

Positioning and layout

In the same way that it is useful to have all deliveries brought to an entrance away from client areas, all dispatches should be out of routine sight. The ability to achieve this will depend on the layout of the site. Where it can be achieved, some form of service yard is the best solution as it can keep the frontage clear of service vehicles and waste removal. Corner plots can be particularly difficult to create an area hidden from public view, because there is no rear area, just two fronts and two sides.

A further general point is to consider whether or not items such as clinical and pharmaceutical waste need to be stored in premises built to the same specification as the rest of the structure, or whether some savings can be made in building costs.

Mortuary/cadaver store

The most sensitive aspect of storage is the cadavers of former patients. In the same way that a veterinary surgeon or practice can build or destroy a reputation by the care and sensitivity taken when dealing with euthanasia, respect for dispatched patients needs careful management.

Most practices have routine collection of cadavers, possibly on a weekly or twice weekly basis. Storage of cadavers is, almost invariably, in chest freezers of varying types. Alternatives would be cold rooms, walk-in freezers, or in areas with no temperature controls whatever. Thankfully, that latter option is now uncommon.

The domestic chest freezer is designed and powered to store prefrozen food purchased from supermarkets, and to freeze small volumes of ambient temperature items such as fresh meat, home-cooked meals, garden produce etc. The appliance was never intended to freeze down a body-temperature dog even of relatively modest size. The device is, therefore, working at the limits of its capability or beyond. The physical design of a chest freezer with a top opening lid makes it extremely difficult to load with a large dog. Once frozen, this must be immensely difficult to remove. Where possible we have installed simple hoist devices to aid loading and unloading.

The alternative would be some form of chiller room or walk-in freezer. These could have racking along the walls, so that bagged cadavers are 'laid-out' with a little more dignity rather than being dumped on the floor. Such facilities are relatively rare as they do take space. It may, however, be possible to purchase a free-standing cold-room secondhand or to have one built within an insulated room.

In the same way that most practices would find the idea of cadavers going to the local tip or a knacker man as totally unacceptable in the first decade of the twenty first century, the body freezer may well be unacceptable by the second decade. The animal cremation industry is still in its infancy and the old ways have not been history for long.

There are plenty of stories about clients asking the practice to dispose of their deceased pet, only for that client to change their mind once Fido is a misshapen block. There are further tales of practices trying to thaw Fido out with a hairdryer to put it back into a reasonable shape before that client calls to collect.

While it is fair to say that cadaver storage is best located so that the funeral service can collect in a professional and discreet manner, it is also true that most dispatches from euthanasia normally take place in the consulting room. It would be useful if it was not too difficult to move those bodies to storage without carrying them the length of the premises, particularly as that may be close to the theatre! The linking passage behind consulting rooms is a useful route, although trolleying bodies away may be well worth considering.

Bagged clinical waste

Many cremation services also handled bagged clinical waste, removing both at a single pick up. Not many years ago that waste did not exist. Most would be considered general rubbish being removed by the council dustcart with a small percentage of the content being bagged into the freezer. As regulations have increased, so has the heap of yellow bags to be held in stock until collection. Normally, space can be arranged in the freezer room. but it must be planned so as to avoid the room becoming a tip.

Pharmaceutical waste and sharps

Sharps are relatively easy as the containers are small and easily stored. A section of the freezer room can be used to store sharps and pharmaceutical waste without taking up very much space. The storage of pharmaceutical waste, although more bulky than sharps, should not pose too much problem as long as an area has been allocated. It is, however, important that pharmaceutical waste is stored securely. You would not want the liability or the publicity if some idiot looking through your bins at night decided to sample some old tablets or inject some drugs from a vial.

Routine waste

Many practices now dispose of routine waste such as packaging and office waste in the large commercial wheeled bins supplied by contractors or councils. Some have these standing outside while others opt to house them under a lean-to shelter or within stores. These bins are unsightly and, wherever possible, are best housed out of easy view. They do take up considerable space and thought is required to determine the logistics of housing and emptying.

Where space allows, it is useful for a veterinary practice to have some form of enclosed service yard. This can be the disposal route for many items and the delivery point for others. A screened off area would allow a vehicle to back in for loading, with the rear out of sight of the clients and neighbours with rubber necks and wagging tongues.

7

In-Patient Treatment

Preparation areas

In the evolution of veterinary practice design, preparation areas are seeing the most radical change. As the range of animal treatments expands, so do the pre-treatment requirements.

The original concept of a preparation area was to provide somewhere where animals were prepared for surgery, with anaesthetic induced and the site clipped and prepared. This avoids the operating area airspace being contaminated with hair clippings and should reduce the level of infective agents.

If all preparatory work is undertaken in a dedicated area, the need for infection-harbouring clutter within the theatre is greatly reduced. This means that the operating room is easier to maintain as a 'high-clean' area and, in fact, can be smaller. Thinking of the preparation area as the hub of a wheel, all treatment areas can radiate off like the spokes of a wheel; theatres, dental, recovery, wards, X-ray, etc. This approach has, in fact, been a mainstay of practice design for some years, though things are beginning to change.

Many veterinary surgeons will have drooled over photographs of American veterinary practices with massive preparation areas, large central work stations and wide-open spaces. A cynic might say that land must be cheap across the big pond and rates calculated on a different formula. As the range of treatments expands and veterinary practices grow, the concept of having a single hub may no longer offer the best solution. The area could become too busy or so large that it becomes a tiring and noisy place to work.

Rather than go for the huge central preparation area, which is mov-

Figure 6   **Preparation area as a hub**

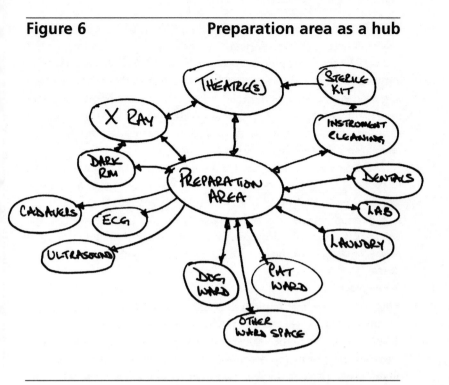

ing away from the hub, a more effective solution may be to change from unicycle to bicycle, with a link – more like dumbbells or a figure of eight. One hub for pre-surgery, one for other in-patient treatments both with a clear central area and the work stations all around. Wherever possible the various working areas, whether they be a dark room or an operating theatre, should have logical links, like the dark room close to the X-ray, theatres close to the anaesthetic induction points, and so on. The aim should be to minimise crossing back and forth across the area.

A further advantage of this hub design is the potential saving of space. Most property designs work on square corners and rectangular rooms. This may be fine in a house or office, but what real use are four corners in operating theatres? Three is more than enough! Chop off one and give it to the prep., do the same with the X-ray room and other spaces. Angling doorways from the preparation area can create work space, avoid right-angle turns with trolleys and save money in terms of floor space.

While some of the work areas off the preparation need to be closed spaces, others can be open-plan bays, helping to give a more airy feel and better communication between colleagues. Glass viewing windows between theatres and the preparation area can also add to the open feeling, even where space is tight. When considering the preparation area as the supply route for all in-patient treatments, it follows that instrument cleaning and sterilisation, laundry and a range of storage should be in, or directly accessible, from this space.

When planning the layout of any work area, and a preparation area in particular, there is a need to take into account the procedures and working methods of the practices. At times these thought processes can help develop improved working practices which can be worked into the layout. What must be avoided is creating a design which will impose unwelcome change in working methods on a reluctant practice.

Piped gases

Most veterinary practices developing their in-patient treatment areas opt for the extra investment in piped gases, particularly oxygen. While it adds to the cost, the investment pay-back is considerable, just in terms of the cost of the consumables. The move to piped gases saves all the moving and clanking of cylinders. Anaesthetic equipment can be wall-mounted in a fraction of the space taken up by a trolley which all makes for a clearer, neater feel.

The installation of piped gases requires the services of a competent specialist contractor. While the pipework may look like standard copper piping, it is specially degreased and requires specific solders, connectors and testing. As the installation is relatively expensive it is useful to plan to minimise pipe-runs as far as possible. This planning should not be allowed to restrict best use of the workspace or best practice, but it should be possible to locate all anaesthetic locations reasonably close together.

All piped-gas systems need some kind of indicator or alarm to warn of low pressure. Some may opt for completely manual changeover, though many will prefer a manifold where supply can be switched from an empty cylinder to a full one by the push of a lever. Select the installer with care to ensure a quality finish. One good point is that gas supplies can be surface-mounted. This means that this installation can be undertaken later, if the budget is running tight.

Instrument cleaning, sterilisation and supply

Used surgical instruments need washing, packing and sterilising. The best approach for supplying the theatres and other points of use is for sterile kits to enter via a dedicated sterile cabinet, with used instruments leaving by the theatre door. Wash, pack, sterilise and store is the normal routine. These functions should be together so that a logical approach can be taken: sink, worktop, autoclave then sterile cabinet. The sterile cabinet is described in the later section dealing with theatres.

Often, the sterilising function is designed within the preparation area. We tend to opt for a work bay next to or between theatres. Sometimes this is screened off, sometimes not. The area must be well ventilated to reduce condensation and dampness from the washing and sterilisation process.

Laundry and cleaning

While smaller practices may combine sterilising, cleaning and laundry, the ideal would be to have them all separate. You do not want the risk of contaminating clean instruments with soiled gowns. The utility room approach with laundry and cleaning materials in the same room is fair, but still not ideal, particularly if the practice uses an outside contractor for cleaning.

For most practices the laundry needs to house a washing machine and drier, with enough space to dump dirty, and fold clean, laundry items. Washed animal bedding can be stored in the wards, drapes in prep. and gowns in the laundry or specified changing area, i.e. a dedicated laundry does not need to be all that large.

Washing machines and dryers tend to be noisy and the atmosphere damp. Enclosing these within a dedicated room with good ventilation and reasonable sound insulation can make life a little quieter. In terms of equipment, the choices are between domestic or commercial units, free standing or stacked. While expensive, the commercial units are more robust, have a greater capacity and will last years. Many are offered with maintenance contracts, guarantees or rental deals, but they are not cheap! On the other hand, domestic models are cheaper and almost disposable items.

One point that should be raised is the potential problem of water regulations. Many water authorities insist on a clear air gap break between water supply and washing machine. This stops any risk of foul water siphoning back into the mains. This requirement is sometimes referred to as a 'type A' air gap and the washer used should, ideally, have such a device.

Another dedicated area specifically for cleaning materials is a great help. Mopping buckets, floor scrubbers and all that paraphernalia can be a storage nightmare. A good deep sink that will easily take a bucket, possibly a sluice and safe storage for cleaning chemicals, will avoid clutter and contamination elsewhere. These things do, however, take space and cost money and compromises may be required to keep within a budget.

Diagnostic rooms

A few years ago a practice I had designed followed their relocation with an open day for small animal clients. As the practice was quite close I dropped in to see how the day was going, and there seemed to be clients everywhere.

We had spent a good deal of time adjusting the layout of the preparation area to meet every considered requirement and, in particular, the X-ray room. I was looking forward to seeing how this area was promoted to practice clients. There on the X-ray room door was a large sign 'Imaging Suite'. This brought home very clearly that practices have moved on from X-rays as the only imaging technique. In this particular situation the X-ray room had been designed large enough to house the ultrasound equipment. Having both imaging techniques undertaken within the same room would not be a problem or be unlikely to create a diagnostic bottleneck, at least for some years. Larger practices, however, may well need to consider carefully what diagnostic procedures can share the same space and which need to be separated.

X-ray facilities

The X-ray room design which best suits an individual practice will depend on a number of factors, least of which is the throughput of animals. The major factors relate to the equipment to be housed within. The principle of the X-ray room is to have a radiologically protected space to stop the operator and those around getting zapped. This, in fact, is quite simple to achieve in terms of design. The harder part is to change some entrenched approaches to X-raying animals.

The danger from X-rays occurs in the split second that the button is pressed and the image taken. There is no reason why the operator has to be in the same room as the X-rays when they push the button – it's as simple as that! While many modern X-ray units operate on a standard 13 amp plug, who knows what power supply will be necessary in the future? For this reason a sensible approach may be to provide the room with a separate supply direct from the fuse box, rather like a domestic cooker.

In fact a 30 amp supply, fused at the service board to whatever is actually required, offers scope for most future occurrences. Walls are easily protected by using a construction of blocks covered with barium plaster. Barium plaster is expensive if compared with ordinary plaster – which is cheap. It is not all that dear particularly when compared with lawsuits!

The next most important risk area is the X-ray room door. Specially purchased lead-lined doors are available, but can be expensive and may not be suitable. A good strong fire-door with a lead-ply cover may be less expensive and just as effective. Lead ply is, as you may have guessed, plywood with one of the plies being lead rather than wood. The tricky bit can be around the door frame but, again, it is not that difficult for a competent builder to sort out, using lead flashing under the door architrave.

If you intend to press the button from outside the room, you need a little bit of clever wiring and a viewing panel. This panel can either be a window in the door or a separate panel through the wall. It must be glazed with a suitable grade of lead-equivalent glass. Such glass is very expensive per square metre, but is purchased on size, so a 450 mm (1'6") square may be sufficient.

Returning to the subject of size, it is quite possible to provide a very adequate X-ray facility in a remarkably small space, depending on your approach and equipment. A lead-lined trolley, a small X-ray machine mounted on a swivel bracket on the wall and enough floor-space to stand and prepare, would all fit in about a two-metre (6'6") square.

If, however, you have a track-mounted X-ray unit, a large table with a moving base and want a protected area within the room to press the button, you are quadrupling the floor area. Add to that the space needed for trolleying animals into the room and transferring them to the table, and you can end up with a very large area indeed. The size must fit the requirements. Money saved by buying an enormous ex-NHS X-ray may be spent on creating a sufficiently large protected room. If, however, you are big in X-rays, then a large space may well be highly justified.

When designing your X-ray room you should consult your radiological protection advisor, who may want to highlight certain factors. Some planning authorities, or building regulations departments, can get quite twitchy. I recall being forced to lead-line the underside of a flat-roofed extension containing the X-ray room. Even though we had stressed that the X-ray unit was pointing down, building control was concerned that anyone standing on the flat roof might be affected.

'Who would be up there?' I asked.

'Possibly a window cleaner' came the response... Checkmate!

Fair enough, the ceiling should be protected if people are routinely in an upper room, unless the floor structure can be proved sufficient.

Where piped gases are installed the X-ray room will require both supply and scavenging. Agreeing the appropriate position should take into account the working area and the way in which the patient is situated on the table. On some occasions it may be difficult to imagine the final layout from plans, as there may well be certain alternatives. Wherever possible, this layout should be agreed before the gas installation is finalised, though this can often be decided after the walls are up and you can see the overall scale of the space.

The X-ray warning light should be on whenever power is supplied to the unit. A competent electrician, properly briefed, should have little difficulty in sorting this out. One solution is to have an over-ride switch activating both the light and power supply but the best approach will vary depending on the particular situation and type of equipment.

Dark room

There is a direct link between X-ray and dark rooms which should, logically, be close together. With a large X-ray suite there may be a good reason for providing the dark room within that area. I would, however, expect to see the dark room positioned beyond the potential danger zone, the other side of radiological protection. This would permit, say, a nurse to be developing a plate, while the radiologist takes further images. In most situations I tend to place the dark room next to the X-ray room. It is often easier to protect and ventilate, as well as giving more versatility to the way the two spaces are managed.

Creating a truly dark room with door and ventilation is quite a challenge, particularly when you want to avoid wasting space. Within the dark room space can be saved using an outward opening door; a good fit and proper door sealers can create blackness around the sides and across the top. A light seal along the bottom, particularly if no threshold strip is used, is slightly more difficult but, again, a good seal can be achieved.

When it comes to ventilation, you do need to get the specification correct. Most extractor fans will let in light, but there are purpose-designed units which are not expensive. The developer needs a cold water supply and drainage. This is the minimum requirement, although quite a number of practices like a sink installed, with hot and cold supply. If this is purely to aid cleaning it can be quite a costly addition in terms of space, and should be considered with care. The blackout in the room should be created by the exclusion of light. This may be a supremely obvious statement, although the point being made is that the interior decor does not need to be black. In fact there are times when you want the space to be quite light and bright.

One factor, which many find difficult, is getting the safe-light wired correctly. The overall light switch should turn the power on to the main bright light. Within the room a second switch should switch off the bright light and activate the safe-light. This offers complete protection from someone, or you, switching on the main light at the wrong time. A lock on the inside of the door is a useful added safeguard though in this day and age it must be like those doors in toilets, which can be unlocked from outside using a screwdriver or coin.

Of course, the dark room could be considered a waste of space. It is likely to take up over two square metres of floor area and, normally, a good bit more. Many automatic processors can be fitted with a dark-box at the loading end, allowing them to be situated in any convenient space. This could be an alcove next to the X-ray room, or free standing against a wall in the preparation area. I do know, however, that many practices prefer the perceived security of a traditional dark room. Once, when I suggested the concept of not having a dark room to one client, he referred to these devices as 'fission fumbling' which I thought quite descriptive.

Other diagnostic areas

Taking X-rays is a procedure often directly linked to surgery, though not necessarily at the same time. It involves general anaesthetic but not scrub-up or surgical site preparation. Remembering these points help position the facility within the preparation area, in relation to other features. Ultrasound and other diagnostic procedures may involve certain preparation, but often not general anaesthesia. These procedures while needing to be close to animal wards may be better away from the surgical preparation area. This is particularly true if clients wish to accompany their pets during diagnosis, say for pregnancy scanning.

Surgical and non-surgical preparation areas may be one idea, or some other form of linked but separate approach. Much will depend on the practice priorities, case throughputs and available budgets. It is, however, interesting food for thought. When it comes to the overall space requirement for a diagnostic room, that will depend on the procedure, equipment and storage. For ultrasound alone a similar space to a consulting room may be all that is required. If there is any significant storage or your ultrasound is a large ex-NHS machine, the room must be much larger.

Veterinary surgery is, of course, moving into totally new areas of imaging, some of which is highly demanding in terms of design and not to be considered by the faint-hearted. The idea of installing an MRI scanner may seem quite out of the question to most private practices, though these installations are being considered by others. One difficulty is that we are talking a new technology where what is installed today is out of date before it is commissioned. Technology has a habit of being simplified and costs can crumble, leaving a practice with a heavily depreciated asset.

Some years ago I was asked to design a special extension to house such a scanner. This was to be the latest thing and much less expensive than those huge electromagnetic jobs of before. Despite that, it was still hugely expensive and the room had to be screened from radio-waves with a special construction and hefty concrete. Although research was done and the extension designed, I was delighted that the development did not proceed. There was a certain inevitability that technology would change and, sure enough, it did. Being on the cutting edge of technology can be a painful place to sit. One step back brings lower input costs and improved reliability.

Laboratory

While not requiring access for animal patients, the laboratory is still a diagnostic room. Samples may come from the consulting rooms, the preparation area, housed animals or from visits.

When deciding the location of a lab within a practice, there can be a significant dilemma. Where ground floor space is at a premium, you may wish to locate the lab upstairs, out of the way. Sadly, however professional you think your team might be, it is likely that more tests would be carried out when the laboratory is close at hand. An ideal location would be to have the laboratory close to the consulting rooms and the preparation area.

Most veterinary practices have some level of laboratory equipment often limited to blood chemistry and microscopy. Others may have quite extensive laboratories possibly with separate staff. Whatever the size, there should be worktop, storage, sink and refrigeration. For microscopy there is a need to sit down, so some knee space should be planned in, as should plenty of power sockets. This can be achieved by using a dado cabling duct, where sockets can be moved or added with ease. Access to the computer system for case records and a telephone are also useful in this area.

Operating theatres

For the majority of veterinary practice clients the thought of surgery brings a mix of wonderment and fear. Around twenty years ago veterinary practices began to avoid the name 'veterinary surgery', opting for 'practice', 'clinic' or 'group'. This was, in part, an attempt to present a less brutal image of the procedures within. For a veterinary surgeon undertaking surgical procedures almost daily, the concept is routine. For the animal owner it can be a time of great emotional stress.

One of the major principles of an operating theatre is, or should be, to have as high a level of cleanliness as can practically be achieved. If the overall environment is clean, the contamination risk to a surgical site should be minimised. It is, of course, the degree of cleanliness around the surgical site, and of the instruments used, that form the ultimate arbiter. This is like a target – the nearer the bull's eye, the higher the demand for cleanliness. The term 'cleanliness' has been used on purpose. Try as anyone might, it is difficult to imagine how an entire operating theatre could ever be classed as sterile, nor the surgeons and support staff within. Sterility is for the site of the surgery, not the entire room.

Having visited a large number of veterinary premises over the years and seen a great many facilities termed 'operating theatres', I have great admiration for the ability of veterinary surgeons to keep a surgical site sterile while working in a room that could not be termed clean, even by a short-sighted observer wearing rose-tinted spectacles. 'We don't have a separate preparation area, we prep. in the theatre'. (Oh no you don't, you theatre in the prep!)

One of the most efficient ways of reducing the risk of contamination is to make the theatre a dead-end: one access door and a no through road. By this simple approach access will be restricted to those who need to be there and foot-traffic reduced. A further concern is the concept of combining the theatre with any form of storage or, for that matter, worktop space. Worktops tend to become cluttered, store cupboards attract dirt, and neither can be routinely and easily cleaned. In fact, the easiest room to keep clean is a totally empty room, finished with impervious surfaces. If that is agreed, so too is the fundamental approach to a theatre design.

There are, of course, a few essential pieces of equipment to consider. Good, shadow-free lighting with an added ability to concentrate light on a particular area. The overall shadow-free light can be achieved

Figure 7   **Sterile cabinet**

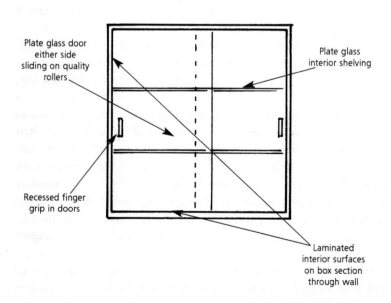

Plate glass door either side sliding on quality rollers

Plate glass interior shelving

Recessed finger grip in doors

Laminated interior surfaces on box section through wall

with four fluorescent lights set in an open-centred square. A ceiling or wall-mounted theatre light can be added to give that extra direction. The floor area remains clear. With piped gases all anaesthetic equipment can be neatly mounted on the wall, next to the balancer unit for the waste gas scavenging system. Still, the floor remains clear. The only essential which needs to be floor standing is the operating table. Positioned under the four-square lights and your theatre is almost equipped. During surgery there will be a need for visiting equipment, including an instrument trolley and other paraphernalia. All this can be removed for cleaning when surgery ends. The room is then clear with only the table feet as a potential bug trap.

The concept of a sterile cabinet was mentioned in discussing the preparation area. This is a cupboard built through the wall between the theatre and sterilising area. Both faces of the cupboard (in theatre and prep.) are sliding-glass panels mounted on high quality rollers. Within the cupboard are glass shelves for storing sterile packs, sutures and suchlike, with plastic laminate interior surfaces which are easy to clean. The cupboard houses theatre consumables and instruments and is supplied from the preparation area side. As well as looking neat and keeping the equipment clean and safe, the glass sides help add lightness and visibility. There is the added benefit that, say at night, a veterinary surgeon can see that a sterile kit is available before commencing any procedure. A minor point, but important.

As discussed earlier, level floors are increasingly needed in animal handling areas. The days of the macho young vet, carrying a prostrate obese Labrador from room to room, kicking open doors along the way, have gone. The era of the trolley and of health and safety regulations is upon us all, like it or not. This factor, together with hygiene, has an impact on the design of the doorway between preparation and theatre.

Having scrubbed up outside the theatre, you need to be able to enter without grabbing a door handle. To trolley the same route, you do not want to be holding open doors and side handling the trolley. The answer is a swing door with no handles. Scrubbed up, you back through the doorway and trolleys you push through. Standard door widths are normally 760–840 mm (2' 6"–2' 9"). A door of this size, swinging back and forth, could be a little painful if it caught you unawares. Also there may be times when you need someone beside a trolley, possibly holding a drip. Double swinging doors with a total open width of around 1200–1500 mm (4'–5') may offer a fair solution.

While some practitioners like the clear, heavy duty, plastic swing doors, I feel they appear somewhat industrial. They also scratch and discolour over time. Good timber doors, with viewing panels at the top, kick plates at the bottom and crash plates where the trolley hits them look good, close well and last for years.

Wall finishes

As discussed earlier, there is no ideal finish for operating theatre walls. The ideal surface would be impervious, with no joints, would last for years and would not discolour or go out of date.

Bearing in mind the earlier comments relating to cleanliness and the concept of a target, the walls of an operating theatre should not be in too much risk of contact with the surgical site. The risk that joints in the surface, particularly impervious joints, could harbour bugs which can make contact with the patient seems a little overplayed. As a consequence, let me remind you of the attractions of ceramic tiles with the addition of waterproof grout.

While a tile can crack with a heavy impact, the surface is easily cleaned and will resist routine scrapes and scratches. The greatest danger is that the colour or style chosen will date, just like wallboards or vinyl. There is, of course, good old boring white.

At the time of design it is well worth considering the likely growth of surgical procedures within the practice. As a practice grows there will be a direct relationship between clinic throughput and surgery. As technology and techniques develop it is likely that there will be an increase in procedures requiring longer periods of general anaesthetic. A long procedure may block theatre space, limiting the ability to handle an emergency case.

While some practices like a large theatre with more than one operating table, greater flexibility as well a reduced risk of cross-infection would be offered by two smaller theatres. In this situation, one theatre could be reserved for procedures requiring higher sterility, at least for much of the time.

Some years ago I was particularly pleased with a veterinary practice developed in a conservation area. The premises were created by restoring and extending a range of dilapidated outbuildings and a redundant barn. Working within the constraints of a conservation area there were some interesting features, including the high, sloping ceiling in the operating theatre. This made the room quite stunning to the eye. I had arranged to show a new client around the place as he was thinking of a conversion project which might require similar approaches. As we arrived I was taken aside by one of the partners and asked if we really needed to look in the theatre. He was clearly a little edgy. Using some rare diplomacy I discovered the source of his concern. One of the assistants, or so he claimed, had nicked a tiny artery while operating on a dog's ear. There in the theatre was a thin splattery red line running from half way up one white tiled wall and right across the ceiling.

In fact, the incident caused light relief in the course of the visit and led to an exchange of stories from all sides – most of which could wear out the carpet of a particular property late of Belgravia. While I never went into the logistics, the theatre had returned to its pristine condition the next time I visited and the premises won three design awards, one a national prize.

Dental areas

Small animal dentistry brings with it various factors which present the practice with particular dilemmas. The fact that the descaling procedure blasts particles and bugs into the atmosphere should keep it out of the operating theatre. It is, in fact, hard to imagine a better way of contaminating an entire room. These airborne invaders have health and safety implications for veterinary and nursing staff or anyone sharing the same airspace as the blasted off bugs. The logic is to try to confine dentistry to an area where contaminants can be controlled, mostly by a good extraction system. As veterinary dentistry has grown over the last decade or so to become a major income source for the practice, so too has the benefit from having a defined area for dental work. To a large extent dentistry has been seen as a preparation area procedure.

For many years we have been designing some form of 'dental bay' within the preparation area. Normally this is centred on a tub table which can double for other duties. As awareness of the air contamination risk has grown we have begun to isolate that area. Initially it was a work bay, then a partially screened area with powerful air extraction and we are now moving towards a separate air space – in effect, a dedicated dental theatre. In some practices the pressure on the dental area means that a second tub table is being installed for dirty jobs in the preparation area. In effect, we are back to earlier designs but with an extra operating theatre purely for dentistry.

Veterinary dentistry brings with it a range of gadgets, most of which need to be close to hand. Some may be floor standing, others need a narrow worktop or shelves. Creating an area where all dentistry will be undertaken, even if other procedures may use the space, works well for most practices.

A great advantage of dentistry as a source of veterinary income is that a great deal of the work can be undertaken by nurses. These nurses should, however, be working under veterinary supervision with clear guidelines. If, as in the medicines' legislation, the word 'supervision' is to be within 'sight and sound' some form of observation window or glazed upper wall can be useful.

The individual practice must decide how facilities for dentistry are to be provided, based on the expected turnover of dental cases. Those who have no facilities at the time of design may find it hard to imagine how many cases can be handled if surgical facilities, and veterinary time, are freed from this routine.

One difference for dental procedures, at least in most cases, is the fact that there is no pre-procedure site preparation, just the anaesthetic induction. Dental cases, therefore, do not need to be prepared in the preparation area as the animal can be taken into the dental room for the anaesthetic to be induced. This avoids the requirement for an anaesthetic point just outside the dental room, as needed for surgical theatres.

Having an enclosed space 'dirty theatre' can have advantages in the central hub design. The enclosed room can be a useful place for inducing anaesthetics in difficult animals, particularly feral and trainee feral cats where handling is tricky and escape a real risk.

Section 3

Farm Animal and Equine Facilities

8

Special Requirements of Farm and Equine Work

When planning the various sections of this book, the original idea was to have separate sections on facilities for farm animals and horses. Once drafting began it became obvious that while the actual animal handling requirements were very different, a considerable number of shared aspects could be better covered in a single section. Also a great many practices undertaking both equine and farm animal work do not actually have any facilities for handling animal patients at their base, but they do have some special design requirements to cope with these clients.

People within the veterinary industry, who have a few more miles on their clock than they would prefer, will recall the days when every market town had one mixed practice. Those practices, in theory, did everything. In fact many of those practices concentrated on farm work and the odd horse. Some almost actively avoided domestic pets as much as possible. Today many market towns have no mixed practice. The original practice remains but is totally small animal and often is one of several in the area. Even the term 'mixed practice' is difficult to define. The business may in truth be 90 per cent small animal with the remaining work coming from a few farm clients, and possibly some horse work. Perhaps the term 'mixed practice' is more a term of approach, attitude and commitment than actual fact. In this section we will consider the design implications for practices dealing with horses and food-chain mammals. We will begin with the design aspects they share then consider the more specialist facilities.

Clients, vehicles and boots

Farm and horse clients visiting the practice premises arrive in a variety of vehicles and are dressed as everything from squire to squalor. Some are a very different breed from your average small animal client which can cause some challenges in the practice that is truly mixed.

For a practice which has no small animal work and just a farm animal or equine base, the approach is to design the reception set up to suit the market. Those trying to cater for all have some early decisions to make, relating to the reception area and how large animal clients will be handled. Some large practices have totally separate reception areas for small and large animal clients. The success and economics of this approach will depend on the throughput of clients. In most cases where clients cross the small/large divide we prefer to create separate entrances but a single reception point available from two sides. This avoids the problem of double staffing or the dreaded 'Please ring the bell' notice.

Decisions about the approach to the reception area will depend on the type of large animal client being catered for, and the volume of visits to the premises. To some extent the nature of their visits is also of relevance. A dairy farmer entering a smart small animal facility straight from winter silage feeding would feel uncomfortable in such an environment, and the trail from muddy boots and the lingering aroma will not be too conducive to the softer pet environment. Those farmers and horse owners trained to leave their boots at the door may well leave a trail of straw from their socks, which might be only slightly less unsavoury.

One great advantage of having a separate farm and equine entrance is that the service inside, and the products and promotions around can be tailored to meet the individual

Figure 8   **Single shared reception with separate entrances**

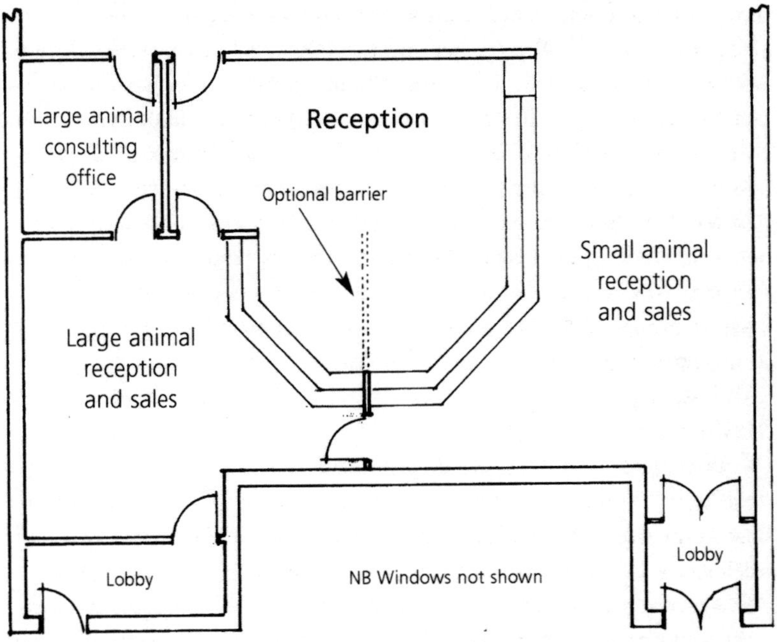

Large animal consulting office

Reception

Optional barrier

Large animal reception and sales

Small animal reception and sales

Lobby

NB Windows not shown

Lobby

Large animal entrance

Small animal entrance

clients. There can also be an area where the farmer or horse owner may be received and items discussed out of general earshot. This could be a small office like a consulting room but with a table, chairs and a link to large animal records.

Horse owners and farmers may arrive in a variety of vehicles whether or not they are carrying animals. The farmer, calling in to pick up supplies having taken animals to market, may arrive with a trailer behind a 4 x 4 or tractor; a horse client may call in when returning from an equestrian event. Being able to handle these vehicles separately from private cars can avoid blocking up a car park, manoeuvring problems and even the odd dent here and there. Even the creation of one long space reserved for such vehicles where the client can drive in, park for a while and drive out without turning is a great advantage.

Large animal support facilities

One of the greatest changes for many mixed practices is the way in which the services they provide have separated. The small animal facility is now smarter, cleaner and presented to appeal to the pet owner. This is no place for filthy gowns, muddy boots and calving jacks. There are, of course, a wide range of facilities that can be shared from accounts and office space to instrument sterilisation, laundry and medicine storage. Keeping farm dirt out of the small animal areas while allowing access to shared facilities is a design challenge. Below are set out some ideas which may help mixed practices marry their large and small animal support facilities. For the solely large animal practice, whatever the farm and equine mix, many of these points are useful but may be not as relevant if pet species and their owners do not attend at the veterinary centre.

Large animal utility room

While many mixed practices do without one, some form of large animal utility room can provide an area for cleaning and equipment preparation without trailing muck through the small animal areas. If this is positioned with an external door but linked to a passage close to the sterilising area, medicine store and other shared areas, it can provide that essential dirt barrier. This is one room where I quite like the idea of ridged quarry tiles on the floor or even concrete with a slip-resistant epoxy paint. Add a central floor drain and a hosepipe and you begin to gain a very adaptable unit.

The way in which this utility area is fitted out will depend on the size, investment and degree of separation wanted. In a large area there may be room for a washing machine kept for farm gowns or a large pressure steriliser, large enough for farm-sized equipment. The essentials will include a large sink, either industrial-sized stainless steel or a Belfast sink, storage for large animal equipment and space to unload car stocks to sort them out, remove pharmaceutical waste, sharps and such like. If the floor space is large enough it may be a room that can be used for the odd umbilical hernia operation on a calf or a ram vasectomy. Where this is envisaged we try to keep sinks and utility items at one end, with some protective barrier between units, washing machines and animals.

Outside this area, adjacent to the door, should be a boot washing point. One of the most practical I have seen was a fair-sized Belfast sink

Figure 9   Large-animal utility and covered area

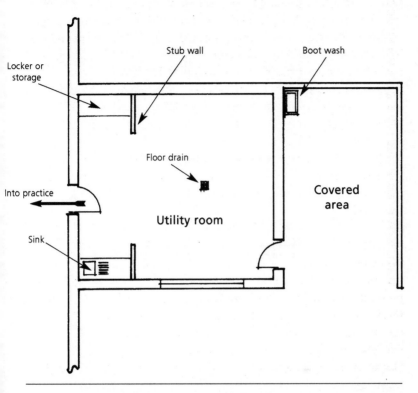

set on brick pillars. The internal base of the sink was at a similar height to a normal dining chair, a comfortable height to rest a booted foot. This had the luxury of both hot and cold water, though a cold supply with a short hose and a churn brush on a rope would suffice.

One minor addition which will add to the value of this area would be a covered area outside this utility room, where cars can be unloaded and a Land Rover or similar farm vehicle reversed so the back is under cover. While the covered area is a boon to all large animal practitioners for restocking their vehicles, it comes into its own for farm practices with sheep clients. Bring a ewe in for lambing in the back of a 4 x 4 or van and it is at just about the right height to examine without breaking your back.

From a useful utility area we have moved, by stealth, to a simple but effective support unit where the odd large animal procedure can be undertaken. The process described is, however, how many farm animal

Figure 10

Utility, covered area plus accommodation

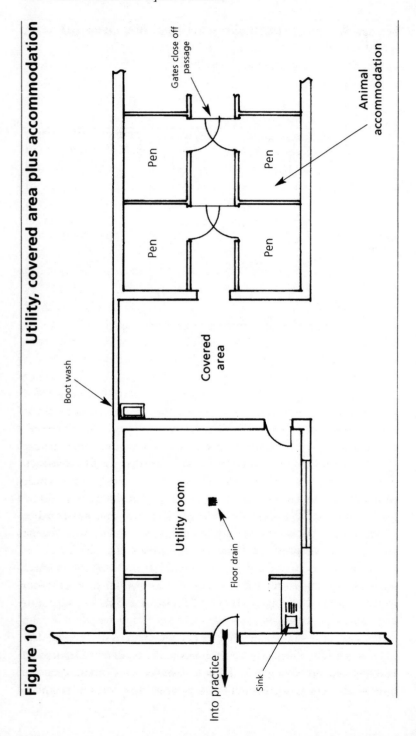

facilities begin to be developed. This is where farm animal premises' development can score over the small animal equivalent. Small steps, with fairly modest investment, can allow a slow but steady growth in the animal facilities.

Farm animal accommodation

There was a time in the 1960s or 1970s when it was thought that farmers would bring their cattle to the veterinary premises for almost all surgery rather than the vet operating in field conditions. While this move did not seem to progress far, there were some facilities built. Some years ago I designed a small animal operating theatre, dark room, X-ray room, cat ward and preparation area, all within a former farm animal surgical unit which had not been used for decades. All that was left was a small farm-utility room, with access to a covered area outside.

Unless you are involved with embryo transfer in cattle or other specialist areas of farm practice, it is likely that the holding facilities required would be for sheep and, possibly, the odd calf. Usage is likely to be sporadic except around lambing time when work may be flat-out. The key aspects are, therefore, adaptability with a low cost of construction and few continuous overheads or maintenance problems.

Whether you opt for purpose-built, permanent pens or some form of adaptable structures within a larger space will depend on your practice approach and species' mix. Agricultural shows and sheep sales seem to manage remarkably well with wooden hurdles and baler twine to create secure but adaptable holding pens. One step up would be interlocking galvanised tubular steel sections, slotting together to create various sizes of pen, all within a larger building. If the peak of use is seasonal, I would tend to favour adaptable penning, so that the space could be used for other purposes at different times. I have even seen such a building with borrowed chairs, hired space heaters and sponsored wine and nosh used for farmer meetings in the autumn.

When it comes to positioning a structure for sheep and calves, there is a very logical place. That is the other side of your covered area from the farm utility room. Such a layout works superbly and is so very simple to develop in gentle stages.

The animal accommodation building does not need to be particularly grand. The farm-type portal frame structure, a converted lean-to building or a fairly simple building will suffice. Any services such as heating, power and water should be capable of surviving for long periods of no use. The ideal space heaters are the instant electrical types, such as infrared strips. Water systems should be drainable with instant, in-line heaters with no holding tanks. This provides a simple, adaptable and ignorable unit.

Loose boxes

For large animals, such as adult cattle and horses, accommodation requires some form of loose box. In most cases we will be considering horses and ponies rather than cattle for reasons discussed earlier. At this stage we are considering animal housing as accommodation and not a space for surgery requiring knock-down.

For those considering one or two loose boxes or even five or six, it is likely that the most cost-effective approach is to purchase prefabricated, timber-framed units from a specialist horse accommodation manufacturer. While the traditional box size is 3.65 m square (12′ square) they do produce larger units, linking tack rooms and suchlike. If one box is to be used for X-ray, the most logical radiological protection is to line the internal walls and door with lead-ply. This is plywood with lead bonded to one side and is what might be called a standard special order item. By this stage you are really beginning to get serious. You may begin to want a level floor for height measuring, a manege, a swimming pool and the lot. The real fun begins and the budget starts to rise when knock-down surgery is considered. Before we move into equine surgical facilities, we would spare a thought for loading and unloading horses and for that matter other large farm animal species where required.

Loading and unloading large animals

Few veterinary practices will need to unload more than one or two large animals at a time and in most situations the farm species dealt with will be the smaller species or young stock. Much of what is said below is, therefore, more pertinent to equine practice, though not at all exclusively.

Many horses are quite adept at walking up or down the gradient of a lorry or trailer ramp, due to regular travel. Others are not! In some cases animals being delivered or collected may be reluctant due to their condition, or under stress. Where space permits a specially prepared loading and unloading area can reduce any gradient and ease this handling problem and risk of injury.

Figure 11   Horse and farm animal loading ramp

Side elevation

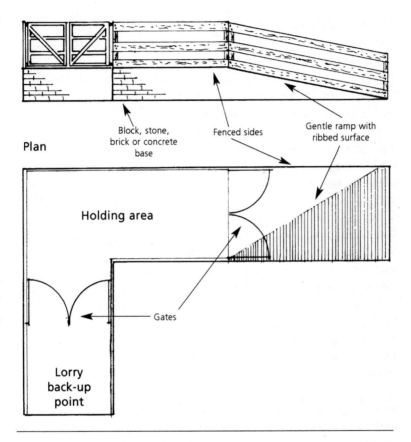

Block, stone, brick or concrete base

Fenced sides

Gentle ramp with ribbed surface

Plan

Holding area

Gates

Lorry back-up point

What is needed is a raised, solid platform which is fenced on either side. The raised area will greatly reduce the steepness of the tail ramp of the vehicle so that the patient mounts or dismounts on a much more gentle slope. The platform needs to be long enough for the animal to be held in an area to the rear of the platform and a gate closed behind them. From this platform there should be a far more gentle slope for the animal to enter or leave. Ideally this should be at right-angles as shown in figure 11.

Figure 12   Knock-down box and preparation

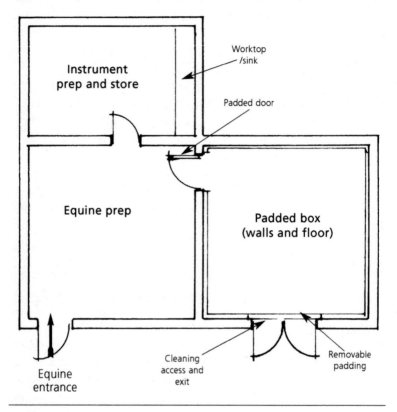

Instrument prep and store

Worktop /sink

Padded door

Equine prep

Padded box (walls and floor)

Cleaning access and exit

Removable padding

Equine entrance

The knock-down box

If the aim is to be able to anaesthetise the odd horse, possibly two to four per week, a simple knock-down box is sufficient. This is a larger than normal box with all surfaces padded to avoid injury to a thrashing horse during recovery. In most cases walls are padded to a height of around 3 m, using a range of materials from heavy-duty foamed rubber covered with P V C to non-specialist finishes. The floor should also be padded, ideally with some tougher material. One of the finest padding materials is a foam lining used in quarries to line the inside of gravel hoppers. It has two layers of padded foam, the surface layer being very tough indeed.

When planning even a knock-down box there is a need to consider surgical preparation. Horse shoes and shoe nails do not mix with padded floors and walls or even recovering patients. This means that the horse must have the shoes removed prior to knock-down and, ideally, any sharp hoof edges smoothed to avoid injury to patient and padding.

A simple padded box with some preparation area may be adequate or even a luxury for many practices dealing with horses. The great restriction is that you can only deal with one animal at a time from anaesthetic to firm standing recovery. Throughout that time your entire surgical facility is occupied by a single patient. This is not a problem with low-throughput practices and adds a valuable service for clients, as well as extra income and interest for the vets.

The range of surgical procedures undertaken in a simple knock-down box may be limited. Nevertheless it can be a valuable asset or stepping stone to greater things. The next step, however, is a huge leap into the creation of a through-flow special unit.

Equine surgical unit

The core of a through-flow surgical unit is the theatre, knock-down and recovery areas. These must be supported by post-recovery housing, preparation areas and a plethora of other facilities. Animals are prepared for anaesthesia and moved into a padded knock-down room. Once anaesthetised the horse is moved, normally by hoist, to the operating theatre table. After surgery the still anaesthetised horse is moved to a padded recovery room. At this point the theatre and knock-down room are free and, after cleaning, both are ready for the next patient. The only bottleneck is if the first horse has not recovered by the time the next surgical procedure is completed. Even then, that animal can be returned to the knock-down box to recover. In most situations this approach is adequate though a system with more than one recovery box can be designed.

The great advantage of this type of facility is that the surgeon is able to work from a solid floor rather than a padded surface. Costs, however, are far higher as there are more rooms, more land, and both the theatre and padded rooms must be designed high enough to accommodate a horse on a hoist. Even when the operating table can be lowered close to the floor, a height of six metres or more may be required. The roof supports or other structure must be of sufficient strength to carry the gantry for the hoist to run along between the various lifting and lowering points.

Figure 13

Equine through-flow theatre design

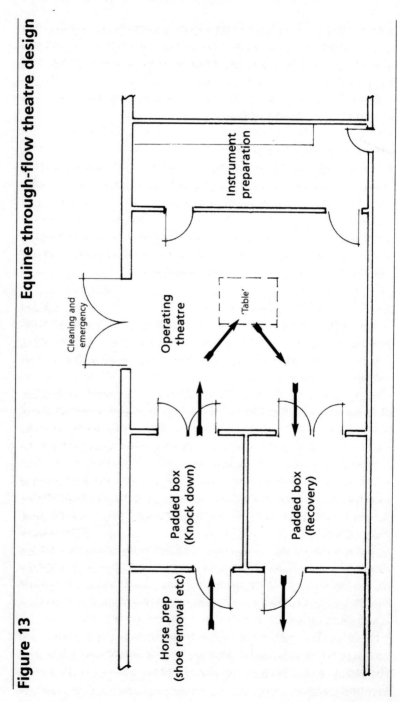

One useful addition is to consider the practical aspects of removal of animals which are euthanased or die within any surgical areas. This is true whether you have a knock-down room or flow-through theatre. You may also need to be able to remove the cadaver with some dignity if the owner is on hand. Having scope to get a vehicle in, or part way in, could be a distinct advantage.

Recovery and housing

At the beginning of this section we touched on equine housing and the choice between 'off-the-shelf' stables and purpose-built accommodation. Where land is available there is considerable scope for remedial therapy and hospitalisation. A large factor in the selection of housing apart from the budget will be the type of patients housed and the work being undertaken. Post-operative recovery, or when continued regular attention is required, would suggest a design where horses and carers are under cover. The 'American barn' approach is ideal, as long as ventilation is good. This design is based on a portal-framed agricultural building with a corridor through and loose boxes either side. If, however, the care is less intensive or more like box rest, traditional stables, possibly with overhanging eaves creating a covered walkway, may suffice.

Paddocks, stocks, a manege, horse walkers and a trotting surface are all useful additions. By this time you will have already installed a level bed for measuring – just to add a bit of colour to your life. Therapy pools and a rolling road come as considerable extras and could only be justified in very special circumstances.

More than in any other area of veterinary practice, the equine sector provides the opportunity for desire to overrun budgets or logic. Those fortunate enough to have the land can, with careful long term planning, build their facilities little by little, as the client base and referral work grows. Here the trick can be to avoid blocking tomorrow's addition with today's development by having some form of master plan hidden away in the dream store. The plan must, however, be based on logic and sound finances. Many equine facilities lay idle for too much of the time to be cost effective.

One alternative to a large site with high investment in bricks and steel may be to consider renting space at a suitable establishment. There could be staff on hand capable of looking after your patients and there may be space to convert an existing structure and create some

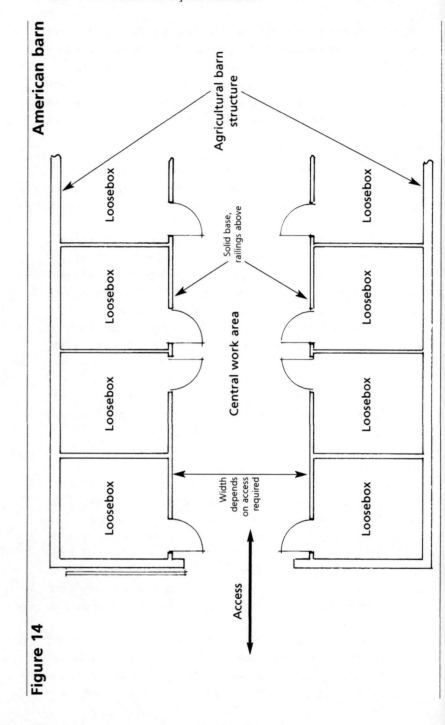

Figure 14

valuable facility without adding strings of noughts to the costs. Many practices have very successful arrangements which form a useful compromise.

The potential problems of this type of arrangement can be in biosecurity, particularly if your surgical and remedial patients are on a site owned by a livery yard. A better arrangement may be on a farm or other base with few horses around.

Section Four

Turning the Key

9

Promotion and Opening

Having developed your new or extended premises there is all the excitement of moving in and beginning to use your new space. This can bring mixed feelings as staff will be in unfamiliar territory for a while, and tempers may be a little frayed for a day or two. Do not worry. If the design is right, everyone will soon calm down and life should be much better.

A marketing opportunity

Having made an important investment, the partners will want to see a return as quickly as possible. When an extension has been developed, there is a risk that the opening occurs but is not marked in any way. This is a missed opportunity to show off your new and improved facilities and gain some useful local media coverage, which could help your investment create that desired return.

It never fails to amaze me how limited is the knowledge of many animal owners about what occurs inside a veterinary practice. While many watch, transfixed by the various vet-based television programmes, they seem to assume that they are different to the local practice. Do they think their bitch goes to be neutered without kennelling and surgical facilities, or an X-ray plate appears by magic? Somehow, there is nothing quite like pictures in the local paper or an open day to impress clients about your capabilities. Do not let the opportunity of a new development pass without maximum yield.

If your development means a physical relocation, there will be a paramount requirement to inform your clients that you have moved. I say that this is paramount because it is – even if you are only moving down the road. I have seen all too often practices make the assumption that because they are in the community and there has been local press coverage of their development, clients will know when and where they have moved. Many may, but many will not.

A strategy and a budget

Whether you are opening a new extension or relocating you need to work out your strategy and, I am sorry to say, have an allocated budget. With a relocation this should be obvious although I do recall a practice who, despite preparing all the leaflets, decided it was not necessary to mail everyone and had some very upset clients and pretty fed-up new owners of their old building.

Let us take the example of a mixed practice which has relocated to a new site which, in all truth, has been designed to extend their small animal facilities. This situation provides the greatest range of promotional options and, if it does not quite apply to your situation, you can select or omit various factors. This scenario has however the new site, pet-owning clients and farmers and/or horse clients. All need informing of the move and there may be varying degrees of mixed feelings about what is happening. For the small animal clients, there are new and extended facilities for the care of their beloved pets. For the farmer, there may be a feeling that you are investing in dog and cat care and reducing your interest in their needs. The same may be true for your equine clients.

The new facilities provide the opportunity to show them off to small animal clients with an open day. For the farm and equine client, there is a need to show that you do still care about them and their livestock. An awareness of these disparate requirements can hint at possible solutions.

First, the relocation is going to require a mailing to all clients on your database, whether that is computerised or manual. There will be the cost of the postage plus an envelope and some change of address announcement. To make the communication more effective, some form of location map would help considerably and why not inform them of the new capabilities you will have? If you are going to this expense why not include an invitation to some event? At least the postage is covered and your building is new and in pristine condition.

Everything is now set, at least in logic, for a relocation notice, brochure and invitation to an open day. This can go to all even if it is directed, mostly, to the pet-owning client base. For many practices it will be the one time you can justify the cost of mailing every single client, so make the most of it.

Open day

Open days are a very special occasion and the sort of event that the local press like to cover. So do invite the press along, perhaps with a special invitation to attend a little earlier than the time the punters will arrive, but overlapping enough for some good photo-opportunities. Add some specially prepared press information, i.e. writing what you hope they will print, and you are beginning to manipulate the media. Oh! What joy!

An open day is a time to show off. It is a time to show your facilities, and your services. Here you come to a decision point relating to balance. You may want to promote pet insurance, flea control, diets and a list of other things, but you still want visitors to see your new premises. The devil is in the detail. Select a few suppliers: vaccine manufacturers, wormer companies, insurers to add interest but not to obscure too much of the view.

Operating theatres look pretty boring without the performing sciences which would not be a good idea, so find an alternative. Set up a large Teddy bear on the operating table, with drapes, a mask and anything else that looks the part. Get some interesting X-rays up on the viewers, some pickled tapeworms, interesting foreign objects and, wow, you are just about there.

The mail shot should go out with the information just a week or so before you know you really are going to move. The open day should be a month or six weeks after you move. This will mean some careful planning of the brochure, but with the printing of the moving date notice left until you are sure.

Official opening

Official openings are very different from open days and can be set to achieve a different objective. Some practices have combined the official opening with a client open day, but this can miss the chance for a second bite at the publicity cherry. In the case of the mixed practice, an official open day may be the time to bring in the farm and equine clients, or they may be invited to a separate cheese and wine, or booze and nibbles, evening.

At the time of writing, our local authority are seeing the completion of a new footbridge across the River Trent. In an official statement, they have said that the decision has not been made whether or not to allow the public to use the bridge before the official opening in six weeks' time. Apart from being a challenge to the local populace to cross the river on the footbridge before the opening which I, for one, intend to do, it does demonstrate that 'official openings' normally occur some time after the actual completion date. The aim is to gain publicity by the presence of a 'name' and to have some kind of plaque on the wall for all to see and be impressed by, for years to come. Whether anyone attends or not is less relevant than the plaque on the wall for all future visitors.

The official opener may be a personality or some form of dignitary or office holder. The latter is probably the safer bet. The hot favourite personality may well fall from grace having eaten a hamster or run over a cat before the plaque has been polished. An office holder, whether the local mayor or other official, is only opening the place because of their position. Lord Lieutenants, High Sheriffs, Town Mayors and Presidents are safer bets than current soap or TV stars. We managed to get an NFU President for one opening, and a World Veterinary Association President for another. (There is something rather striking about a 'World President' don't you think?). In both cases the event was invitation only, aimed at specific clients but, more importantly, the press and the plaque.

Publicity apart, open days and official openings can be great for staff morale and team building. Somehow everyone pulls together for the greater good and silly quarrels can be put aside. Another great motivator and one which helps sum up this book is the actual process of development and, in the case of relocation, the move. Over the years, we have noted that business tends to expand during the development and not just when it is completed. People are nosy and want to see what is happening and there can be enormous goodwill amongst clients and staff. Even when the place is a building site, or a quagmire, the end objective seems to engender team spirit.

If you think about the logistics of relocation, you may need to take some fairly strong sedative, at least until you think properly. When you actually come to the crunch, it is not all that difficult. There is no enormous plant and machinery in terms of tonnage and even the heaviest theatre table can be shifted by three or four people.

Before panicking about the move, think of your client base. This is where mixed practice can score but even with small animal practice there will be some specialist dedicated talent amongst them. Why not ask your client base or certain members of it to help with the move? This could be the greatest act of client building you will ever achieve. A farmer with a tractor and trailer, and enormous muscles, a horse box or some good clients in a hired transit van. Shift the lot, dial up a take-away, and have a party... job done!

Job done? Well not quite! You have a new facility which is bright, clean and sparkling, and now you have to keep it that way. This will require planned cleaning, maintenance and decorating. Invest in a contract cleaner so that your nurses can nurse. Schedule in repainting, particularly when new plaster has been painted with trade emulsion. Planned maintenance will keep your premises looking good for longer and avoid the disruption of major refurbishments. Now... job done!

Index

Pocket Practice Guides

Clients, Pets and Vets   Carl Gorman MRCVS

This is the book that every new graduate trembling on the morning of their first day in companion animal practice needs to have read – ideally twice.   Mike Dale MRCVS *The Veterinary Record*

I very much enjoyed reading this book. ...an invaluable guide for dealing with clients for anyone in veterinary practice at the 'sharp end' of client communication and handling. This is sensible, basic and very helpful advice on dealing with clients.

Veterinary Management for Today

Carl Gorman's book provides advice and food for thought in the pitfall-strewn field of client management. The core message of the book is the importance of communication. Communication with colleagues, lay staff and, most vitally, with clients. Keeping clients informed is the best way of keeping clients happy.

By demonstrating some areas where communications can break down, and the reasons why, *Clients, Pets and Vets* enables you to look after clients and so fully enjoy your time in practice and maximise your potential.

CONTENTS

Why do we need clients? – Making clients feel at home – Making your message understood – Clients have pets as well – The art of persuasion – How to look good – How to break bad news – Awkward situations – Euthanasia – How to be a helpful client

Price	£15.50 (paperback)	**Publication**	2000
Format	216 x 138 mm	**Extent**	176 pp
ISBN	1-903152-04-6	Distributed in N. America by Iowa State Press	

Finance, Employment and Wealth for Vets
Keith Dickinson

...an excellent pocket guide to the fundamentals of the commercial world of veterinary practice. I strongly recommend this book for the practice bookshelf.   Paul Manning *Veterinary Times*

I wish I had this source of information available to me at graduation. It would have made life a lot easier. It is logically laid out and quite accessible for financial information.   A recently-qualified MRCVS

Within a year of first publication, Keith Dickinson, a leading adviser to vets on finance, has already fully updated his useful practical guide for newly-qualified vets and everyone in the profession who is concerned about financial and employment issues.

His discussion of pensions, mortgages, savings and insurance focuses on the key issues for you as a vet or manager: sorting out your priorities whatever the dizzying range of products available.

CONTENTS

Joining the veterinary profession – A salary guide – The interview – Employment packages & taxation – Entitlements of employment – Employee benefits – Pensions – Mortgages – Personal savings – Personal financial protection – Insurance – Interviews with four vets – What next?

Price	£15.50(paperback)	**Second edition**	2001
Format	216 x 138 mm	**Extent**	144 pp
ISBN	1-903152-08-9		

The Veterinary Support Team
Maggie Shilcock

What a pity this book was not written before I became a practice manager! ... an easy-to-read style... a must for practice libraries and for those considering joining a veterinary practice.

Penny Bredemear *VN Times*

...this book is a starting point for providing the veterinary support team with the training tools that they need. ...for new entrants into and the progressing members of the veterinary support team.

Christine Ann Merle DVM MB *Editorial@penguin.doody.com*

A comprehensive and practical discussion of the role of veterinary support staff and their importance to the practice—invaluable for support staff, practice managers and vets. The author, an experienced practice administrator, gives concise advice in a clear text, with plenty of diagrams and drawings.

Key topics include: how support staff create and influence the practice image, how to create co-operative support staff teams. The discussion is balanced by comments from working support staff about their jobs.

CONTENTS
Who are they and what do they do? – The practice image – Client care skills – Assertiveness and dealing with difficult clients – Support staff and money – Support staff and the office – How support staff contribute to sales and marketing – Support staff and the law – Support staff and the clinical role – Teamwork – Understanding other roles – Surviving in veterinary practice – The future

Price	£15.50 (paperback)	**Publication**	2001
Format	216 x 138 mm	**Extent**	144 pp
ISBN	1-903152-06-2	Distributed in N. America by Iowa State Press	